Contents

KU-185-731

	v	The Liver Bards
	vi	Acknowledgements
Philip Davis	vii	Foreword
Thomas Conolly	1	leaves
		The Kitchen Breathes
Katherine Spink	2	Slakehill Comprehensive
Alexei Zadorojhnyi	6	Miranda
		Chinese New Year Party
Dick Gibbons	7	Breakfast News
John Wallcraft	8	Sonnet
Suzanne de Néame	9	Boy
Rachel Malham	10	Ardmoran; August 1990
Gareth Rees	14	Confessional
	15	alwayswaitingsomewhere
	16	Physics 101
Jenny Atkinson	17	Haunted By You
Gavin Lewis	22	Gloria In Excelsius
James Bainbridge	28	17 Rushmore Terrace
Jane Davis	37	The School Caretaker
		Polishes His Taps
	38	Magnetic Tape
Alan Corkish	39	Liverpool, 1981
	40	Electric Memories
Lynn Owen	44	Lessons
Patrick Widdess	45	A Poet
		Central Heating
	46	Overcome
Tom Sperlinger	47	View above Buttermere, 1999

Ben Newton	54	Apart from the flame-haired horse chestnuts
Wendi Bestman-Sharp	55	Autumn Leaf
	56	Enchantment
Bill Dynes	57	Madness
Ruth Talmud	62	All to Zion
		The Hypnotist
Robert Burman	63	Always A Pound
Hannah Sheppard	66	Fragments of a Relationship
Rachael Tunnard	70	To a flexible friend
Andrew Taylor	71	Cathedral I
	72	Addendum I
	73	Lines Written In Early Autumn
	74	Waveform
Helen Harper	75	Millions of Nuts and Bolts
Katherine Bainbridge	85	Emi
	86	Holy Cow
	87	Lucky Sons
Naman Yasin	88	A Journey Back to My Roots
Peter Miles	91	Boring
Meena Chauhan	92	Screaming Silence
		Nothing Lasts
	93	March Attitude & Angry Sighs That Echo Along Into April
Anthony Evans	93	Ambition

The Liver Bards

Editors

James Bainbridge
Hannah Sheppard
Tom Sperlinger

Editorial Panel

Thomas Conolly
Rhiannon Davies
Rowena Lawrence-Thorn

Wider Panel

Meena Chauhan
Ed Denison-Edson
Amanda Peacock
Emily Pickering
Gareth Rees
Lucy Round
John Wallcraft
Nathanial Whitfield

Cover Art Work

Lucy Round

Publicity

Rhiannon Davies
Emily Pickering

Acknowledgements

For help, support, encouragement and believing in us:

Keith Birch
Sarah Coley
Philip Davis
Margaret Gascoigne
Guy Goodwin
Faye Hammill
Zoe Hancock
Sue Irvine
Angela Macmillan
Brian Nellist

For all of the above and for sharing her experience and technical knowledge:

Jane Davis

For the generous contribution of funding as part of The University of Liverpool:

Professor Miriam Allott
Professor John Belchem, The Faculty of Arts
Professor Philip Love, Vice Chancellor
Professor David Mills, The Department of English
The Friends of the University

Printed by Impressions: 16 Palm Hill, Oxton, Wirral, CH43 5SP

Proceeds from the sale of this anthology are being placed in a fund for the production of a similar book next year.

For more information contact: creativeanthology@hotmail.com

Foreword

I remember, some time after I had left school happening to meet a former schoolteacher of mine, not altogether surprisingly, at the local library. He was a published novelist, as well as a teacher of English. As we walked out of the library together, he stopped to exchange a brief word with a quiet, rather drab middle-aged man who was coming in. As we walked on, my schoolmaster said to me, 'That man wrote a good poem once, on the death of his wife, on bereavement. It was an achievement.'

We walked on a bit further, and I asked whether the poem had been published. It hadn't; it was simply that, being a writer, my school teacher was often shown bits and pieces that poeple had done – offered in this case, he said, rather awkwardly and shyly. But my schoolteacher was moved by this poem and, another day, he showed me an unpublished poem that he himself had written about the bereaved man, in response. I remember one line of it – that the widower, unpractised as a writer had nonetheless penned his feelings and 'managed a good day'. But my school teacher said he didn't think he could show it to the bereaved man himself.

I am now a teacher of English Literature at the university. But, years on, this memory sticks in my head, and comes to mind now, I think, for two reasons.

First, that it is not good that occasional one-off poems so often go unpublished, because the writer is unknown or diffident. We lose important human documents which might make us see the human world a little differently: outside that library, I had just seen an ordinary-looking man taking his books back.

Second, that it is very, very difficult to write something even half-good, and that poetry in particular is often uneven, and comes and goes. One line alone may be memorable and, in that, may be enough. As readers, we need to be on the generous look-out for those lines, those moments, of promise.

That is why I am glad of the existence of an anthology such as this: offering a chance of encouragement to the unknown amateur, the young beginner, the local struggler.

The contributors to *The Liver Bards* are aged from seventeen to sixty. About half of them are members of a creative writing group in the University of Liverpool, students who want to write for themselves as well as study. Half again are people from the local community who simply saw an advert or a poster, asking for poems, and sent in their work. It is a good Liverpool mix, for that is what literature should be doing – bringing together in one place people of different ages and backgrounds.

Likewise, there is in these pages a genuine mix of poetry and prose, in a wide variety of styles, beliefs, feelings and moods. And that too is good – because we should not always decide in advance what we like; because writing should be risky and unpredicatable and must be given its chance; because every narrowing of what writing 'should' be like brings with it a potential narrowing of what life can be like.

In such ways, an anthology like this one offers itself as a little image of possibility: the possibility, I mean, of a real community of shared yet diverse interests. Nor was it easy to get published here: out of nearly 200 contributions, 47 have made it from 30 different contributors. It is an achievement.

It is also part of an on-going project devised by the three editors. At the very least, they want to produce another such anthology next year. For that, they need your support, just as the writers need your attention. So as readers, be on the look-out for the good things in this book, just as the editors were, as they looked through the many submitted manuscripts. Mrs Oliphant, a now neglected Victorian writer who once lived in Birkenhead, wrote a short story about a failed painter whose unsold works were left in a gallery, their faces to the wall. 'Turn them round,' he dreams, 'and see what's best in them.'

Philip Davis
English Department,
University of Liverpool

The Liver Bards

Thomas Conolly

leaves

Pastel shapes, translucent as skin
cling to the wetted bough and
like eyeless lids, frail human hearts,
flutter.
Spring: a dark, dank nuisance
blocking someone's gutter.

The Kitchen Breathes

The kitchen breathes a heavy smoke and sighs,
 The silken, silver smoke that lifts and falls,
 And paints a yellowed hue upon the walls.
She washes grease from thick black pans, and dries.
And she has witnessed evanescent skies,
 And sunlight lick the blackened crooked fingers
 Of trees which, like smoke, in memory, linger,
And leave their yellowed hue behind tired stinging eyes.
Yet what of Thales[1], gazing out to sea?
 His heart was stirred by mottled blue-green spume,
The dark cracked pane now echoes his geometry.
And, though we've kissed a thousand lives 'adieu',
 A pulse flits and flutters in smoke, stench, gloom:
A waking dream of ancient forms anew.

---

[1] Greek philosopher (500-600 BC), first of the Milesian School. Though little is known of Thales, he is credited with deducing geometrical rules from observations of ships at sea, and the claim that everything is made of water.

Katherine Spink

Slakehill Comprehensive

"Kaz, have you done the homework?"

Danny flaps his book at me wafting black strands into my face. I force my hair behind my ears.

I sigh, "No, what was it?"

"Sums, page 249."

I check my watch. 8:43AM.

"Can I copy? I'll change some answers."

"Yeah, alright."

Danny hands his scruffy workbook over. I try and ignore the rest of the class and rush the answers into my book. I make sure I add a few mistakes of my own.

What I am copying makes no sense. Maths has mystified the whole of 9R this term. It doesn't help that we have another supply teacher. She was as thin as a rake in September but now she looks like she'll be off with a baby soon too.

Mrs Ringwold doesn't arrive to take the register. Probably ill again. So Danny marks everyone as here and takes it to the office himself. The bell rings so we trudge up the stairs and across the school to Maths. Miss Succubus is in her room with her hunched back to us, rising and falling. I can hear her sucking. She turns around and wipes a banana milk moustache from her face. God, she's got cravings too.

"Ah, sit down everyone." She stands up herself, jiggling her jowls with the movement.

"Take off your coats."

I take my coat off despite goose pimples. We slowly clatter to a halt.

Miss Succubus stares at us intently, "I trust you've all done your homework. Karen, what's your answer to number one?"

I flick my book open to Danny's answers. Is that a 4 or a 6?

"The hypotenuse equals 6."

Succubus' eyes narrow, her cheeks blow out.

"Try again."

"4?"

Out of the corner of my eye I see Danny waving his right arm madly.

Succubus picks on Stinky Sheila.

"Sheila, what answer do you have?"

Sheila doesn't answer at all. She gazes at Succubus with a gaping goldfish mouth. Danny is nearly jumping out of his seat and throwing his arm to the ceiling.

"It's 5! A 3, 4, 5 triangle!" barks Succubus, "You should really know this by now. It's the easy one. You're absolutely hopeless." She glances around the room. We just sit there. She flicks the overhead projector on with a fat finger strangled by a ring that would have fitted Saturn itself.

"Here are some more of those sums which caused you all such a problem. Remember a squared plus b squared equals c squared."

She runs through the entire method of finding the hypotenuse again. Her mouth opens and closes exhaling noise while her cheeks flap in agreement.

Her whole body wobbles.

"Now get on with it! We'll do this until you get it right," she says.

The remaining fifty minutes pass slowly as I doodle around my sums. The sun shoots through the window creating its own triangles of light on my book. I can't concentrate with Medusa over there. Finally we put down our pencils.

"So Karen, 3, 4, what?"

Her look turns me to stone. She sucks the ability from me. I struggle in my book for the answer. It looks like a "6."

"Why do you persist in getting this wrong?" She paces up and down, her heels banging. She comes up behind me and those podgy hands land on my shoulders. The bell rings and I'm up like a shot.

"Homework page 250!" the Succubus yells after us.

At home Matt helps me.

"Just fit the numbers into this equation," he points through the undergrowth of doodles to the rule I copied down from the projector. "And that will help you find the hypotenuse."

Without Succubus glaring at me my head is much clearer.

Then Mum comes in, "Hello you two. Tea early tonight, don't forget."

My mind is empty again, "Why?"

"Don't you remember? Parents evening?"

A shock thrills through me as my brother nudges my arm. Mum has a habit of phoning up the school governors to find out those important events that I neglect to tell her.

"I didn't forget," I claim and I reach for my bag. The appointment sheet is at the bottom of it, crumpled and blank.

"So who shall we see first?" Mum asks me looking at the rows of teachers sitting at their desks in the school hall.

I pretend to check my appointment sheet. "English," I say, because Mr Maple does not have a queue in front of him. The hours pass and no one says anything too nasty about me. All the usual really – "concentrate more" and "could try harder"– but generally a positive reaction.

"That's nearly all of them, isn't it?" asks Mum, "Only I don't remember seeing your maths teacher."

I search the hall for Miss Succubus. "I can't see her," I say, "Maybe she couldn't make it."

"Shall we go home then?"

"I need the toilet first."

"I'll meet you by the front door," Mum says.

The lower school toilets are on the other side of the building.

Rather than toil up all those stairs I decide to duck into the staff toilets underneath the school hall. After all, it's a special occasion. Through the sacred door the first thing I see is Miss Succubus' refection in the wide mirror. She is sucking on a straw that is embedded deep into Mrs Ringwold's ear. I can hear her greedy sucking and the smell of cheap disinfectant is mixed with the stench of greasy fat. The great lump is feeding on Mrs Ringwold's brains! Mrs Ringwold herself is unconscious. In the mirror Miss Succubus' reflection looks up and sees me. Her gaze bounces off the mirror into my face. I turn around to face her. She is still sucking and I can see frail Ringwold wilting with each powerful sup she takes.

I lunge at Succubus, "Get away from her you monster!"

My aim is bad, but I catch Succubus' arm and she loses balance. Pink goo streams out of the straw as it leaves her shining lips. Succubus recovers and throws herself at me. Her weight works against her, I dodge her lumbering attack. But she turns and charges again. I glance around for a weapon. A plunger rests against the sink. I hold it up against the oncoming Succubus. She

4

runs onto it. It sinks deep into her gathered flesh. A whistling noise pierces my ears. I can smell old meat as the air rushes out of her. Her bulk reduces to a pile of sagging clothes hung with rags of flesh. I go to Ringwold's side and shake her awake.

"Wha- What's going on? Oh I must have fainted," she says viewing her surroundings. "Lucky you were here Karen. But what are you doing in the staff toilets?"

When we get back home I tell Matt what happened.
"...And she blew up like a balloon."
"That's a tall story," he says, "Shouldn't you be in bed by now?"
I see he's hiding a naughty video under a cushion.

I decide not to tell Danny, even though he wonders about us suddenly having another new Maths teacher. He wouldn't believe me either. This new teacher has wobbling chins too, and yes, we're doing hypotenuse again. She's set us page 251 and I can't do it with her hot gaze on me like this.

Alexei Zadorojhnyi

Miranda

We used to have a flatmate
who had only two value-judgements,
like 'It's pefect,' or 'It's shit.'
She was the easiest person to talk to,
ever melancholic, wearing black SAS boots
even on her own birthday.

Yet now and again
she would look up dream-bright like one wading
up to her knees in balloons blue and red
to some ultimate potlach
where things are all perfect beyond happiness.
Never tired of long nightly talks, blessedly forgetful
she's still around there,
safe in her wonder as years ago.
But since then we have moved,
and simplicity is vanishing.

Chinese New Year Party

She uncorked a bottle of sunshine.
In the room the air twanged with many new voices.
A dragon's smiling muzzle
was peeping through the window
as somebody argued
bestraddling a chair
that friends are not really enough
to make you happy.
"At night, when the moonflowers dance across the floor,
sterilizing your presence,
you better be alone."
But hardly anybody was listening.

Dick Gibbons

Breakfast News

Alone, on this wet Thursday morning, somewhere deep in April and not too far from the central promenade; Elizabeth Duff, switches on the wall mounted television to the breakfast news and butters bread with sorrow for the flickering, cathode-ray, hymn of despair. She stacks the thin wafers of bread with the reverence of Bibles beside the grill and considers the hanging of the curtains in the lounge-cum-diner, mounting a stool to do so.

Unseen from this high position, the televisual medium; her Technicolour font of all, informs her that Beijing is making new trombones. At last! Happy news! She rejoices for the recovery of the eastern brass instrument industry. Music will fill the air over China.

Only she has misheard. Beijing is making neutron bombs.

John Wallcraft

Sonnet

Eternal girl who murmurs through all song,
What evil trick or dream has brought you here?
To where each house is temple to your wrong,
And doors are closed upon the once most dear.
Could you yet wake to know a life of Spring,
And see your face in dews and bursting leaf?
Such heavy stuff ne're takes to fretted wing,
A walking dream, a parable of grief.
Too late! She cries, to live in such conceits,
Too hard to turn when turning frames a sky,
Between sun blocking hands raised in defeat
She blinks out tears from such sun-darkened eyes.
       She lives only in our dreams of pardon
       Once and happy daughter of the garden.

Suzanne de Néame

Boy

Paper-thin boy, thin reeds of hay hair
With your book and your pencil
I can see you behind me.

The station, the train, the tracks and the grit,
Are sepia-faded, my head-locked timetable ripped
By the spikes of the hair on your chin.

You cough and I answer in time;
Feet shuffle, I edge forward so they seem
(In a vision my own) to be dancing with mine.

You weave pencil through fingers,
Scratch knee, check watchless wrist for the time.
Purple raincoat eclipses you, with ugly grey skin

So I step forward, aware through glass to the left
Of the train (which departs)
And touch your hair-exposed arm in the mirror,

Lean forward to sloping nose, kiss the lips bent
Into blue hard-back and wish
For this moment again and again we will kiss.

Rachel Malham

Ardmoran; August 1990

Early evening, late summer. The West of Ireland. Everything is green; mountains and fields hum silently to their ancient rhythm. The brown earth is cracked and baked from too much sun this year, *It was a hot one*, people had said, *Turf will be ready early*, they had said. The air is heavy with the aroma of dried peat. Midges buzz and gossip in the long grass, wasps whisper in the wild gorse. This silent panorama awakens to the intrusion of a motorcar engine. This memory that it is, in fact, the twentieth century, seems totally discordant with its surroundings. The black Fiat looks wrong, out of place, as if this was all a magazine, and a child had drawn it on in obscene black ink. It pulls up on the embankment with a start. Doors open to release the children (two girls and a boy) like greyhounds at the beginning of their circuitous race, flying through the air, across the grass, claiming this as their territory, delighted with themselves because they were here first.

I remember slowing down, letting the others go on ahead, my ten-year-old legs starting to trot instead of run, not through lack of being able to keep up, but rather because I was waiting for the adults. For my Mother. I was worried about her. She had been quiet in the car and she was never quiet. Everyone else had been chatting and laughing, but she had been silent, looking out the window, seeing things I couldn't see, silent movies of the past. Because it wasn't true, we hadn't got here first, she had. Her and my Uncle. This was their field, their ground, their space to run and do cart-wheels, not ours.

I didn't realise until that morning, when we were told we were going to Ardmoran, that I didn't know where my mother came from. I hadn't had to, she had always been there with me, as far back as I remember. There had been no need for questions. I knew she came from the West, but my Grandparents had lived in my Uncle's house in the Midlands and I hadn't really imagined any-where else. I had never seen where she was born, where she grew up, the house that had sheltered her as she figured out who she was going to be. I wondered if she had her bed by the wall like I do, if she had posters on the walls. *We didn't have posters in those days*, she told me when I finally asked her, much later. I looked back at her as the adults advanced towards me and the other children left me behind. She looked different, uncomfortable. She was walking with the other adults, but her mouth was still set in that oddly silent line. *It can't be easy for her, especially so soon after Mammy's death*, I overheard my Uncle say to his wife.

I hadn't really known my Grandma but everyone says she was lovely. My memories of her are like a hazy dream, one of those ones that when you go back to sleep you try to bring back, but never can. I remember she had white hair and glasses, and sat in a huge throne-like chair in the corner of my Uncle's house, next to the range (or *The Aga* as we would call it in England). There she would pray, click-clicking her rosary beads, knitting out hope for us all. She didn't just pray, she sang too, sometimes, and she talked most of all. I suppose that was where my mother, and me, and my cousin Sarah ultimately got it from, *The Gift of The Gab*, wrapped up nicely and passed down from generation to generation. And that's what I remember, my Grandma praying and talking and giving me green pound notes to take to the local shop to buy sweets, sitting in her chair, or on the wrought-iron bed, which was safely watched over by a picture of The Sacred Heart. It scared me, that picture.

And that's what I wondered, as I watched my mother approach; I wondered if there was a similar picture in this house, and I thought how unfair it was, that she had always been with me and knew everything about me, and I was only beginning to discover who she was.

The wind had begun to breathe through my black T-shirt, carrying with it the voices of the other children, calling my name, entreating me to come to them, for they had reached the house. I could see them ahead, the colours of their clothes, my cousin Sarah in white, and my brother Richard in blue, who was two years behind me but always two steps ahead of me, climbing on some stones and waving.

Nothing prepared me for the sight of the house. When people had said cottage to me I had imagined it to be like the cottages I had seen on holiday in Devon the year before, whitewashed and thatch-roofed. This was nothing. *A place among the stones.* For stones were all that was left. Grey, moss-covered stones. The four walls still stood, but only just. There was no paint, no roof, no floor, only mud. I imagined that the roof had blown off in a storm, like the house in *The Wizard of Oz*. I advanced towards it with a mixture of horror, shock, and fascination. This couldn't have been a house. Could it? It wasn't big enough. It was tiny. My head swam with questions. Where would the bathroom go? Where were the bedrooms? The stones only marked out one room. Surely that wasn't all there was? The walls were different heights so it was hard to tell how high they really had been. Deceptive.

I went through the door – that is to say, the break in the four walls. Sarah and Richard were already climbing them. They weren't high, but they were slippery. The moss and lichen made it difficult. Despite the heat of the summer, the inside of this house, and all that lived in its shadow, was damp. The mud was soft underfoot. I remember thinking about that: the mud, the soil. The soil was the reason we had to leave here. Our placenta had stopped feeding us.

As the Seventies began, this soil had breathed its last, it was weary, it was tired. I imagined calloused hands running through it, desperately trying to touch it with life, silently asking its permission for us to stay here a little longer. Struggle and soil instead of struggle and toil. The two go hand in hand and have for years, I learned later. As I made tracks in the damp mud with my trainers, as I wrote my name there with my feet, I remembered pictures my mother had shown me once, drawings of people who had starved to death, something to do with the soil, the potatoes – I wasn't too clear on the details but I remembered the pictures – they were horrible, scary. Ghoulish faces with green juice coming from their mouths, writhing in agony. *They had to eat grass to survive, our ancestors*, she told me. *Struggle and soil.* When we moved from here, the house began to crumble, and as the stones fell, we did too, but lies, feuds and battles over land were the storms we had to weather.

They had been happy here, our family. I saw a photograph once, years later when I was a teenager, and I was shocked. In the photograph, it looked like a normal house, white walls and a table, and my Uncle Tom laughing with my Grandma, who in this photo had neither white hair, nor glasses but looked like an older version of my mother. It was full of surprises, a box of tricks, that house. It had untold stories within its silent stones. It stands alone in a wild wind-swept field, this monument to us, this vacant womb, battered by winds and weathers, but the stones remain.

I started climbing and looked to my mother, who was leaning against a large rock, looking at the house, still far away, eyes with a film of tears and I knew that now was not the time for questions. I expected her to tell me off, to tell me to *Get down;* the rocks were loose and dangerous, I might fall, I might get my clothes dirty. I wanted her to; I wanted her to be herself. I remembered once finding her at the kitchen sink in our house in London Suburbia, hands lost in suds, eyes somewhere else, crying softly, singing *The West's Awake.* She was looking out of the window, but beyond the pens of terraced gardens. *We are so closed-in here, As good as battery hens*, she said. Today was like that day; wanting to be naughty just so she would come back from the other place she'd gone to, to tell me off. Only now, here she was, and she was still somewhere else.

I climbed down from the wall. The stones were cold and damp and I didn't like it. It was getting dark. The day began to embrace its inky death as I ran my hands across the walls, the dampness, the memories that weren't mine and yet belonged to me somehow, and I left the house. I began to run. For no reason whatsoever, but because I could. We were not battery hens. Not here. Here there was space to run and air to breathe and limitless sky that didn't look like the lid on the world, but like freedom itself. I ran and ran until they called me back. My mother's voice, my name, the wind.

As I returned to them I could see my mother smiling, sharing a joke with my Uncle, reliving a memory they shared. She was smiling broadly and she was back. I smiled too, with relief, as she ruffled my hair and said *Time to go.* But the truly ironic thing, the thing it took me years to discover, was that the soil had claimed me and I couldn't ever leave, not properly.

It's in the blood, the people say.

Gareth Rees

The Confessional

Fling open the doors and
Enter if you will
With chest stretched broad
Relieve yourself of the outside drains
And unleash the arbiters of our time.

But be sure to bow, eyes to the tiles,
As you take your sanctuary on noble granite
For bitter vengence pours on those head-high.

Through weakends and weekdays,
Here is the place
Where battles were planned,
Fights were fought.
In the sanctity of the temple
Against the loyal altar,
Confessions are bought and prayers said:
Here is where Tommy met Johnny
And Ronny hit Tommy.

The other is outlawed, here
In the candid bowl.
Golden streams converge between buts,
Unifying man, binding the bad with the good.
For those in the ugly struggle of the world outside,
There lies The Box, with white necked Father Doulton
Sitting in expectance.
He judgeth not, only carries the heavy load.

Neither weak nor strong,
Young or old,
Happy or sad,
Solid or liquid
Are refused here.
Donations are always welcome,
The bowl takes all and relieves all.

14

alwayswaitingsomewhere

*i*n some unknown cloud
or in some blue sky stipple
in a pudd*l*ed ripple
or a swimming crowd

i'll be mouthing your truth
smiling   y*o*ur pride

in some ra*v*en verse
or in some strumming train
in a shattered pane
or a mother's curs*e*

i'll be singing   *y*our soul
crying   your colours

in some foreign mile
or in some childhood wood
in a street where we stood
*o*r a space we'd smile

i'll be dancing
                your time
        chasing your tears

in some rainbowed bough
or in some reigned rosehips
in a time of low lips
or of screaming *how*

i will be waiting sitting
                soft-beating
                your heart

Physics 101

"and he was saying...
...like, oh my god..."

and I'm thinking
                    No
            I'm
            very far
away from him at the moment.

THIS IS THE REJECTED GRAVEYARD
people die here...

                              This space
                              This emptiness

            ...was
            never written
            or warned
– It can't be expected

There
            is
THIS BRUTAL VALLEY OF REJECTION
It is never hunted
It grows wild without soft hands

constantly alone with other invisibles   I wait
and yet I hate the pushing rain,
though it gives me a club and a home.

There is no choice.

                        The resting cave of reality –
                              the ultimate
                              solitude
                              of existence

Space
            is
                        so
                              full

16

Jenny Atkinson

Haunted By You

The journey from Gatwick had been a nightmare as usual and the last thing I needed when I got back to my pad was to find an ex-boyfriend hanging around.

Literally.

He was a bit blue, his head was at an angle that usually denotes he's fallen asleep in front of the telly, and his body was like a limp Guy. And the smell…death did nothing for him.

I immediately stepped back out of the room and shut the door.

I would have considered keeping it shut and hoping it would go away, had it been the spare room. I had enough on my plate as it was. But no, it was the master bedroom, my bedroom. I was not happy.

I mean, why do break-ups have to be so messy?

I was quite annoyed at him, to tell the truth. I mean, I'd told him he was welcome to use my flat while I was away, to soften the blow. I didn't expect him to abuse my trust like that. And I'd made such an effort to be nice.

I'd planned my words carefully. Tried to emphasise the fact that while I still loved him, I was no longer in love with him. Told him that if you love somebody you should set them free. Said 'it's not you, it's me'.

Told him that with the help of a good surgeon, and a few tips from Dr Comfort, he'd be a catch for any girl.

I followed all the dating etiquette. I did my bit.

I mean, I may not be the nicest person I know but I didn't want to break him.

Anyway, I was at a bit of loss as to what to do with the damn thing. I mean, what's the protocol? Dial 999? It seemed a bit melodramatic. I mean, Will's days for emergencies were long gone. I thought of phoning the local police station, but I wasn't sure I had their number. I decided that Barnaby downstairs would know what to do.

It's generally better to get a man to deal with this sort of thing.

I knocked on his door.

"Oh Barnaby," I said emotionally. "I need your help...I've...discovered something horrible." My top lip quivered fearfully. It sometimes pays to play it heavy on the abverbs, I've found.

Of course, he followed me upstairs. I think he was grateful to be the one I went to for help, to be honest. I pointed to the bedroom door.

I thought it would be nice to make him feel manly and strong, so I did the whole melodrama thing.

"A body!" I shrieked and covered my mouth with my hand, like I was about to vomit.

Barney set me down on the sofa and handed me the box of tissues, which, incidentally I'd bought for Will's sake. I'd guessed he would take it hard.

"Stay here, babe, I'll check out the scene," he said.

He threw open the bedroom door as if he was expecting to surprise an armed robber. A moment later, I heard him retch and gasp and sigh and, I think, even snivel.

So I made occasional sobbing noises from the front room, to make him feel better. I've found men can handle themselves much better if they feel they've got someone else to be strong for.

But after a while I got bored and decided to have another look, just to, you know, see.

So I went in and sat on the bed and you know, it was quite a weird experience to look up to Will.

I couldn't help thinking of the times we were sitting in the front room together and he'd just take off his socks and start picking at the dead skin on his feet. I mean, eugghhhh. And that was like, our third or fourth date. I know it's awful, but for a split second I was glad.

"He's dead," Barry said in a grave voice.

He'd hung himself from the swirly wrought-iron decoration at the top of my wardrobe. With the tie that I'd given him for Christmas. It took me ages to choose that. From my dad's drawer. But hey, it was only Christmas Eve I met him, I didn't have chance to buy anything.

He looked quite funny, to tell the truth. Floating in the air, with his body all heavy like that. I imagined him hovering across the room, like a zombie, heavy lifeless arms in front of him, pro-pelling his body forward.

But I think my imagination had run away with me 'cos for

18

a split second I thought I saw Will's head lift slightly, and wink at me.

I stepped back in alarm.

It was the trauma getting to me, I decided. It might surprise you to know, I'm quite sensitive. These things effect me in a very deep – even spiritual – way.

But then Bradley said,

"Take it easy, babe, you're looking pale."

Pale? I'd just spent two weeks in Australia! So I just glared at him. Which he somehow took as a come-on and walked over and tried to put his arm around me. I shrugged it away of course, and as I did so, something fluttered to the ground. It was a piece of paper addressed to me.

I picked it up.

Basil shouted "Don't disturb the evidence!" But I opened it anyway.

"Dear Nicole," I read aloud. "Ever since I first saw you, 17 days ago, you have been my everything. It was Christmas Eve, you were in Marks and Spencers struggling with your shopping, and needed my help. When I saw those sparkling emerald eyes, ruby red lips, and coal black hair, how could I say no?" I wasn't sure I liked the coal bit. I bet you thought I was blonde. "But I can understand we cannot be together in life. Our love is just too intense, too great; infinity cannot be contained within the narrow constraints of life… blah blah blah… spelling mistake…bad syntax… I have devoted my life to you. My death is a tribute to you. Love, forever, Will." How nice.

But I'd had better, you know?

So I went into the front room and pulled out my file-box of love letters. I can never throw these things away. It's one of the things about me; I'm very sentimental. And to be fair, this was my first suicide note. I filed it away under 'W' (I don't do surnames)

But anyway, Bartholomew was still in the bedroom, doing nothing useful, so I said,

"Look, the smell is annoying me, will you call someone and get them to take it away? Phone the local police station?" I was getting a little bit impatient by this point.

"Oh…okay." He said. This seemed to snap him out of hero mode and he began to talk normally. "My phonebook's downstairs. I'll just nip down and get it. But don't worry. I'll come straight back up. I won't leave you on your own. I'll support you through this!"

I wasn't happy about that, he was getting a bit too close for comfort, so I said.

"Actually Balthazier, I think I need to be alone right now. I… need some space to clear my head."

I've found that watching soaps is really good research for knowing what to say at times like that.

Of course, he protested, but I eventually persuaded him to go, and to call the police to come and pick it up. I mean, *Friends* was on soon, and men are an annoying distraction when you're trying to watch TV. They do gross things like slurp tea loudly. Or pick the dead skin off their feet.

So anyway, Bob left but just when I thought I'd got rid of one problem, this was when things began to go really wrong. I went to shut the door to the spare room before settling down to watch telly. But as I did so – I kid you not – Will's head lifted and he smiled.

"Hello again," he said.

And I'm like: Hello? Reality? Come back!

Then he did this weird kind of thing, and sort of jumped down out of his body. It was all getting a bit surreal and I don't mind telling you, I was freaking out. And there he was, looking just like he had when he was alive, only he was sort of see-through and as he walked towards me he passed straight through my bed and my bedside table. But then I thought, no, that's going too far.

"You're not a ghost, you're a cliché!" I said in my nastiest voice. I figured, if that was his game, I could do scary too.

He just sort of smiled, and walked past me into the front room, and sat on the sofa.

And then he said to me, like everything was normal,

"How was you holiday? With 'Mike'?"

He obviously envisaged us having some form of civil conversation, which I supposed was better than some tacky chain rattling thing or whatever ghosts are into these days. So I sat down on the armchair furthest from him.

I didn't know what he wanted from me, and I was a bit surprised that he knew about Mike. So I just said the holiday was okay.

And he was like,

"Just 'okay'? Isn't he the love of your life? Or is he just another guy you use – like the one just now? I thought you were going away on your own to find yourself?"

He said it all quite calmly.

I was thinking to myself, I don't have to answer to you, you don't exist. Something must have happened between dying and death, 'cos Will was acting all smug and superior. I'd never bought the sensitive guy bit anyway. I was glad I had dumped him.

So I said, a bit sarcastic like,

"I was having trouble locating me. I needed a little bit of help..."

And he said,

"You always do. But you dump someone as soon as they stop being useful to you. You're afraid of commitment. You're afraid of forever."

I wasn't going to stand for being insulted in my own home, so I said,

"With good reason, judging by you. If you're what eternal life looks like I'd rather...die."

So then I decide, to hell with 'don't talk ill of the dead', and tell him the truth about what a disgusting, ugly slob he is, and how I don't want to put up with his – or anyone else's – horrible habits for the rest of my life.

And then I tell him to leave.

But he just keeps on smiling that annoying smile and says, quite sweetly, "no."

And that really scares me. So I shout,

"I don't want you! Get over it! Piss off! Find a nice ghost girlfriend!"

And he just says, casual as anything,

"I'm going to show you what commitment really means,"

And then what does he do? He pulls his feet up onto the sofa, pulls off his socks, and starts picking off the dead skin.

And he's been there ever since!

Gavin Lewis

Gloria In Excelsius

*'There is the same
world for all of us, and good and evil, sin and innocence, go through
it hand in hand.'*
    Oscar Wilde, Lady Windermere's Fan

I
Don't Be Such a Prude!

As we walked away
the clouds turned black and washed with grey,
shrouding the assembled crowd of a suburban cinema
and spitting flecks of April rain
on white macks and black club umbrellas,

1

And Alice my dear,
these wings will tire
and fancy fade and pall.

Alex and Paula, Lauren and Sam
sat in the summer sun under Gavazan Rock
reading reminders and Saturday addresses,
        are we dressing for lunch?
                oh don't be such a prude
and under the look and lingering lies
        is my dress almost clean?
        have I time for a shower?
Shirts to be laundered, trousers to be pressed
a substitute for a Sunday best,
will everyone notice will anyone care
does the hostess wish to stare
that I've a side parting in my hair?

The newspapers and broadsheets are shallow,
they tell of all in this world that we'd rather forget

of cancer and Aids and the ending of days
under a marvellous technological howl.
But 'Dear Johnny' still writes on gilt edged paper
using a special pen with inkwell refill
that makes him feel something special
a 'susurration of syncopation',
and he lavishes and rests and strokes and draws
happier with the printing than the presence.

2

And Alice my dear,
these wings will tire
and fancy fade and pall.

    Would I have presumed to break and broach the matter
make you shoot up from your chair
and set the table and its contents to the floor with a clatter?
These things of indecision, these things that make a man wail -
for a time, for a time.

And Alice my dear,
these wings will tire
and fancy fade and pall.

    Should I have been vain and vulgar
and shouted and caressed at the skin by your collar
sniffed and snorted and laughed with the others?

These things I see
these things I hear,
these things I'll never do.

      Taking drinks at a café
at lunchtime at the least, and the stares
     – (at this time of day?
     Wine and beer,
     a gin and vodka? –
chuckling wares and ways to digress at the best
we'll sing you a song, we'll sing you a song
though don't leave the next round too long.

What'll I do with the rain at my back, down my neck
      What'll I do now the grey clouds envelop
the waiting cinema crowd,
      now the April spits are spitting harsh
and the black club umbrella
      offers no protection?

Inside out
      Alice, dear Alice.

*

*'But – (hand raised in admonition) – but behind
this veil of gentleness and peace night is charging
(vibrantly) and will burst upon us (snaps his
fingers) pop! Like that! (his inspiration leaves him)
Just when we least expect it. (Silence. Gloomily.)
That's how it is on this bitch of an earth.'*
      Samuel Beckett, Waiting For Godot

II
I'll Pound And Pound Upon Your Awful Prose!

      Now pay attention to the ensuing speech
a wattled throat drones to the Mountford Hall,
      Don't take drugs
      this is the Union President
      this is the monetary man – person
and on and on,
and people don't giggle or howl fits of laughter
but restrain themselves and glance at another
      will they remember
      will they forget?
      The Union is here to –
and they stare about them seeking to register

Another three years to pass away
drifting away on Macellan's monologue –

I've wandered now over and over again
the small boundaries of this small world,

watched a young man's plays
played day in and day out,
>What's it all come to Delilah?
>What, Henry, what?
I've circled the drinks table and looked at the cost,
and walked off to drink from the tap

Simple fucking things that appease the simple fucker

A deluge of blondes and brunettes
French Spanish Morrocans
>horticulturalists and agriculturalists
the diseased and the demented,
the wasted lamented lacky

Another three years to pass away
drifting away on Macellan's monologue -

No old bean here causing a frightful scene
worrying whether the tie is loose or loosened
>I'll pound and pound upon your awful prose!

The dear old dear, dear Mrs. Dear,
>have you seen the graffiti on your wall?
>Some young thugs were there last night
>and what an awful sight it was too,
>oh dear Mrs. Dear,
>will you be needing this light,
>do you think? Do you think?

A few beers for bedtime,
>a last laugh at the fool
Mr. Macellan's Monologue.

*

*This profound silence, this great grief; this
entire oblivion of all but one thing, had upon them the effect of
the high altar at Easter or Christmas.*
     Victor Hugo, The Hunchback of Notre-Dame

III
The Knights Of The Faith

I,I,I
I'm not allowed to use I anymore
   objective subjective
a differing opinion

I'm a dying man in a dying land in a dying thought in a dead sea

   'Have another cuppa'
sat in an armchair with frayed cloth covering
patterned with daisies and other memorable things
and an old lady smiles covering a multitude of sins,
   the front door bell rings
and from the dirty streets comes a dirtier man
a reflection of dejection rings rings rings
   you'll stay for tea dear?

I,I,I
want to go back home
   I don't want to wait and smile
   and verbally masturbate
   over this celebration of mundaneness.

These tired eyes have not failed utterly yet
and can gaze once again upon your frightful face
   though they have molested the innocent
   and foundered upon higher places than this,
come then, let's leave here and there,
forget this indecisiveness and derision
and wonder once more at this banal breach of faith;

26

And laugh and joke,
they said.

Who? Whom?
The Knights of the faith,
they danced and japed.

      Would you expect to love me still
when the nose/hair/glasses have been replaced
with a different design and wonderless grace?
      With a sigh I shall resign my looks
and cover over those unread dusty books
that lined this house's ancient walls
and pass them on in some metric will,
in some frivolous, exhibitionist fad
of old age and fag madness
driven to the walls by gin and dereliction

I shall sit down and expect it
resting in the chair with daisy patterns sewed upon it,
sipping tea and smiling inanely
just glad to be an interest for a moment

When the sea that throngs around you
heaves you as a whale on some sapping shore

This frightful sight is all I'll be,
is this really what you'll see?

James Bainbridge

Seventeen, Rushmore Terrace

or

The Absentee Doctor

The rhapsodic growth of traffic, breaking between moss and soil, and bark of morning; gradually triumphant in its nearing peak, shatters stooping street lamp bulbs with a piercing glow through the shimmer of sycamore-lined avenues. Somnambulant bedroom curtains, stirred only by a lamenting city breeze, purr to softly wake those who drew them in the sapphire darkness of the evening before. Alarm clocks and teasmaids, and timed televisions expectantly poise their coiled springs to explode with welcome news that this – is dawn.

Coffee makers are switched to steam. Kettles boiled. Eggs placed in pans, and throughout the building from basement to attic, the mousetrap catches of toasters are each by each depressed, and this – is dawn.

The bright, red geraniums, like pom-pom bull's hearts on tender springs, salute the arrival of the postman in line along the ground floor windowsill. Here the table is folded away after breakfast, the cloth removed and the silver wire toast wrack replaced with a Japanese bowl of African violets.

In the vestibule, a porter on linen apron knees creeps beetle-like to polish a chessboard floor. Post is arranged for a doctor's arrival on a squat walnut table, to the left of the hall. In flat **number five** Marjorie Gross begins a letter to her sister in Peru. All of this is normal. *All of this is true*. And buses, and taxis, and dark, mole-like trains that fly loaded canons past bright billboards, with kissable lips, fill the building's empty offices with the grey dust of life.

Suits pressed. Ties exact. And the porter bemoans the day that he last dusted a hat. For gentlemen these days never wear hats. He's lucky if he'll get to guard an umbrella, and so his polishing continues.

In flat **number four**: a tablecloth. Feather-white,

stretched like a rich membrane across the pustular table then lain, with porcelain service and monumental silver teapot, shimmering like a gaudy pearl. A natural misshapen sphere, perfect in every way but simultaneously ugly, it winks from the centre of the floor.

And behind it, awaiting the guest's arrival sits the Raven, dressed entirely in Victorian black, a large cameo broach at the high noose neck and magnesium white hair held in pain-inducing bun at the back of the ageing skull. Delicate hands, the consistency of paper, rearrange the cakes on the stand. A compact is unfurled and lipstick reapplied to the dry, bark-like lips. The grandfather clock taps its foot impatiently. The compact is closed again. These are not the eyes that used to undress window dressers.

The small glass casement in the **front attic room** illuminates little more than the square of the book Herr _____ is reading. He flicks idly through the translucent pages, disinterested by their now familiar contents while the small oil heater warms his left shin. Placing the book on his dresser, he moves to the desk and begins to write. *Arrived in Vienna, West-Bahnhof, 6 o'clock. Paid station attendant 80 Heller for my two large cases to be carried to the cab. Many officials at station.*

Breaking off, he lays the pen down beside the bottle of blue ink. He feels cold in the room and the heater gives out only a dull warmth. He crosses to the dresser once more and opens a round, silver tin in which he keeps his money, then checking the small red book again, returns to his desk and takes up the commentary:

Cab charged two Krowne, twenty.

Back in **Five**, Marjorie Gross also proceeds with her writing:

Gone are the ones that she said I'd be getting, just the other ones left. The ones that she used for everyday. Not the ones saved for guests; she's left me the second best.

How long has this tea service feud gone on?

The doctor's post remains upon the walnut table, for he has not arrived at work. The small brown and white rectangles with their bright mosaic of stamps, wait; arranged with a carefulness usually preserved for wedding bouquets their neat, ballpoint addresses, uniformly mute, proclaim: Dr. Burchfield, **Flat 1**, 17, Rushmore Terrace.

Directly above the empty surgery, in **number three**, Veronica Ryman stares unblinking at the glass award for up-and-coming architectural excellence. She ponders her years of training, the great ideologies she followed. The way she had been inspired by Tschumi's ideas of architectural narrative. And she wonders how this in any way relates to the positioning of a new toilet block in a down town community centre.

At the top, back of the house, in **apartment seven**, next door to Herr_____, resides a painter (Jonathan) and his lover (Gregor). Jonathan; inhabiting a world of near cut-glass thought and vision, betrays those misconceptions of the subject's beauty, and finds only pleasure in the act of sight itself. It is partially through this credo that the canvas remains white, although if truth crept from beneath his slate facade, it would emerge that Jonathan does not paint largely because he is lazy.

Across the room stretched with a distinct curvature to his back, lays Gregor upon a low, Japanese-style bed. He too is caged in fractal sight, not through over intellectualised procrastination, but by long lashes that veil his eyes from the electric morning sun-light.

Gregor is awaking from uneasy dreams. The canvas has been white for three days. Like a cubist mantis, its easel prepares to pounce through classification from furniture into art, but its wooden limbs do not give for living. Jonathan, as much matador as painter confronts the empty space, but draws back; not afraid, but cautious of disturbing the essence of the void.

In **six**, Herr _____ finishes his commentary. It is all overly methodical, but this is how it must be. Accuracy is everything to Herr _____; it is the foundation to his life. Tonight he will dine at the Sacher as recommended by Karl. He will record everything he eats, how much it costs, the design of the cutlery – anything that may aid him to prove that he was actually there.

Still no arrival at **flat number one**. The porter rubs the brass handle with a tired rag, then exits with his pipe and envelope of shag for the cool brick yard.

Five: *The ones with the chubby handles. The ones that are one saucer short. No pot either. The other was a full service; cake plates, milk jug, sugar basin. Pot. The other ones have gone to you, haven't they?*

The Raven lifts a wing of the black velvet cape to preen, before rising upon slim-booted feet and walking to look outside **apartment four**. The boy said that he would be prompt to arrive. The Raven is not given to waiting. More white powder is applied like plaster of Paris to the grained cheeks. He remembers when boys would stroke his smooth flesh, and smile.

Gregor rolls, shielding his eyes from the sun in **seven** and exhaling a smoker's purr that draws Jonathan across the bare board floor to the bed and the sleek, sleeping form. He strokes the slumberer behind the ears then goes to the corner of the room designated 'Kitchen', and begins to make coffee.

It has not always been this way. Remnants of an existence that awaited the creative cessation are scattered about the attic. A gallery catalogue listing some of Jonathan's least-white paintings. "A Turner for the twenty-first century" wrote the *Evening Standard*, and this canary yellow cutting sings from its clip frame above the empty space.

And Gregor has not always believed himself to be a cat. This is simply temporary: the world viewed through that bulls-eye glass disproportion that exists only between waking and sleeping and that creates those beautiful, momentary, senseless collocations, full of essence; devoid of comprehension. He stretches his toes.

Behind the door to **number three**, Veronica has folded up the plans for the community centre and picked up a copy of Tschumi's *Manhattan Transcripts*. This is what had excited her about architecture in the first place. The way that space could define event, and event space. She turns to her computer and begins to type a letter of resignation.

In **seven**, Jonathan returns to the bed, scowling at the newspaper review. It has left him lost, trying to replicate that way of displacing the concrete, and seeing sight in place of substance. He admires Turner. He admires the drifting, solid essence of air, and light made real and touchable. He wants to paint with such understanding of the abstract, the mundane day-to-day ethereality of existence.

He wishes to control paint as Turner did, as if it were thin silken dreams. He wants to *paint* dreams; make touchable the gauzes that stretch through the violet time, recreating there these vaporous visions.

He kneels beside the feline Gregor on the breathy white sheets of the bed then reclines beside him. And sleep. Sleep is so rewarding now. To paint sleep. He wishes to paint sleep.

I hope that we can resolve this matter. Your loving sister, Marjorie.

She takes a gold label from the drawer of the desk and

applies it squarely to the top right hand corner of the pastel pink sheet:

> Marjorie Gross,
> **Apartment Five**,
> 17, Rushmore Terrace.

Placing the letter in a waiting addressed envelope, she swells like butter pressed through silk and begins her velveteen procession around the cushioned room.

Herr _____ seals another envelope behind the door to six. He places it firmly in the centre of the desk, tracing his finger across the neat blue address. He follows the quivering line with his elegant nail: *Rt. Hon. Sir F.L. Cartwright*. He decided some days before that he should extend the purpose of his stay. He will place himself in the centre of things; make sure that it is undeniable that he has been there. The British Ambassador is surely proof enough.

He opens the draw to his desk and takes out another, small dove-grey envelope. This is printed with the name and address of *R. Lechner, Graben 30*. Into this envelope, he slips four photographs of himself, seals it and places it with the other.

Three: her fingers, lit beneath the halogen glow of the inexpensive, yet stylish reading lamp, take the colour of uncooked salmon as they nimbly pick their way across the lettered tombs of the keyboard. They pause; levitating above the keys, then lift the glass tumbler of water to her lips.

Her creativity has been locked away from her through the prescriptive needs of architecture. She wishes to do something new. She wishes to be a writer.

THURSDAY

Sitting at the desk, she types 'THURSDAY' upon the screen. The letters with their uniform black staves and loops, comprised of tiny dust like specks, await their duplication. Her hands float like those of puppets above the keyboard, then are brought to rest; wrists, dissatisfied upon the wood. She stares out of the window at the empty street and Georgian tenements opposite, listening to the quiet purr of traffic. The index finger of the right hand, as if unnoticed by the slouching left, reaches forward and presses the full stop.

There. A perfectly crafted piece of fiction; today is Wednesday.

She saves the piece onto floppy disk. Satisfied that creativity still pulses within her, she returns to the willowy lines of the community centre toilet block.

One: Still no arrival. Maybe he is *dead*.

Each external, tiny pane of the building, is turned in the breathless air to absentmindedly reflect the copper sulphate ether. Its frontage, a gallery of unknowing Polaroid investments into heaven, melts black gloss portico and eel-like curls of railing down upon the blazing brass plaques and creamy sun-worn steps.

Black cabs, like old, stooping monks creep by, apologetic for their combustion engine cough. And an ice-cream van's distant toil for matins rings softly upon the walls.

Herr _____ opens the wardrobe. Today he will step outside **apartment no. 6** and take a cab to the Karls-Platz. There he will meet with an enemy agent at the foot of the church.

The Karlskirche was completed in 1737 and exudes a fine essence of juxtaposed architectural styles. The staunch Corinthian colonnade sits not quite comfortably against the flowing rococo facade. Herr _____ has often commented in his notes that there is something *not quite right* about the building, and that is what makes it perfect. If the subtle jarring of detail were not enough, the Stanetti depictions of the plague brought doom and squalor to a building of glory and splendour. Herr _____ had written:

It is as if the building has invented itself, piecing together the architectural details it admires despite the impracticalities. Across the square, a statue of Brahms glowers disapprovingly.

Gregor no longer imagines himself to be a cat. Awake now, and with a pneumatic steadiness to his limbs, he lifts himself upright against the pillow and finds Jonathan sleeping beside him. There is somewhere he should be this morning, but his brain still creeps through the burrows of the night. The realisation then stabs him like a fork. He leaps from the bed, hurriedly dresses and flings himself out into the day, slamming the door of flat **number seven**.

The moment when the stem of a wine glass unexpectedly snaps, or an unlit firecracker explodes, or door is slammed, sends Jonathan falling through cotton pillows. The medical term: myoclonic jerk, evades the brilliance of the sensation. Jonathan has felt himself fall. The moment is both familiar and alien, for he had not been aware that he was sleeping, and now he is awake.

The frank, solid door with brass, snake number **five** does not betray the horrors within. Checking to make sure that she cannot be seen from the window, Marjorie lifts the china milk jug from the ravaged card table. The ill-matching pot is drained of tea and it seems a waste to throw the milk away and too great an effort to return it to the refrigerated bottle. She stands, framed, before the high Georgian glass, cradling the jug in her trembling hands. She cranes her neck to make certain no one will observe her act from the street. Satisfied that she is alone, she lifts the cool white vessel to her lips, the smooth rim like the edge of some unnatural shell; and she lets the flow of white liquid trickle over her teeth and between her tongue and her palette.

In **apartment four**, no such atrocity is committed. The Raven stares glumly at a pink cube of fondant upon the cake stand. As he resigns himself to the fact that the boy will not come, the doorbell mumbles something of his arrival. Gregor kisses those grey wooden lips.

The porter stands alone in the delayed decay of the empty ground floor apartment. Nobody has used **number two** since a firm of solicitors; Fourman and Martin, or Martin and Fulman who dealt in conveyancing and expired from boredom. The porter maintains the bright red geraniums, and breakfasts on toast there, and lives the life of the young city gent beneath a photograph of her majesty, until he descends to his knees with wax polish and scrubbing brush.

Back in the heavens, behind the door that is **six**; Herr _____ takes a dark grey suit from his wardrobe. It is to the style fashionable in Vienna at the time, he has seen to that, expressly explaining his very wish to his London tailor with the meticulous pedantry present in all of his life.

He buttons the jacket and neatens the tie with a platinum pin, then opens a drawer to take out the cufflinks baring the crest of some great Austro-Hungarian family. There he sees the troublesome brown, plastic bottle. The stark white label proclaiming his name. He has not taken his morning tablet. He has missed that part of his routine.

As usual he opens, tut-tut, disapproving lid of the bottle, takes out a duck-egg pill and goes to the sink where he pushes it to join all the rest, through the brass teeth of the plug hole. He picks up the thick sheaf of notes and the small red book from his desk and goes to the door onto the hallway. He has an appointment to keep.

Seven: he fell from a pavement and carried on falling. A pavement wrought with multiple constellations of granite crystal, with miniature forests where moss burst between the flagstones. Not that vague anonymity of detail expressed in Turner's impressionism, but his earlier attention to detail with which he portrayed the rise of Carthage.

This was a dream. Not a waking approximation of what sleep is, but a real first-hand experience of the pencil thin masts of the sailing ships. The temple to Dido lit with a buttery richness by the mid-morning sun. Dappled pools of bright translucence upon its statues and friezes. Each with a crisp perfection of detail in its carving.

The coffee is cold and Gregor is gone. But Jonathan has been blind. He cannot paint sleep as Turner paints waking reality, not because sleep is abstract already, but because the imagery in dreams is far from abstract; it is beyond photorealism. Sleep is intense. It cannot be loosened and still viewed as sleep.

Jonathan begins to paint.

Behind **number four**; the Raven pays the boy, and remembers distant times in a coastal port where the rôles were reversed and he would receive the money. *A certain grey flickering of the magic lantern projector dispelled the fire of tar in the street air, and took sailors behind mildew blackened lace curtains, through into the burgundy flock of back parlours. A button opened in the waxy steam of clothes drying before the orangeade illumination of an electric fire. A ceramic Shire horse poised in static toil of the doily earth, standing with gloss hoof eternally raised. The shipping forecast lyrically lapping upon the picture rail, hung with tinted portrait of Errol Flynn and tapestry sampler, sun-sucked of colour.*

The tops of trousers would catch upon the sofa edge, and heavy hands more used to handling nets than nylons, sought harbours only dreamt of whilst at sea. Humber, Dogger, German Bight, *five just the evening, ten for all night. Eyes unsteady from the stillness of land and the readiness of drink would meet with his, and stroke his smooth flesh, and smile.*

Herr _____ steadies himself against the banister. Something is not right. This is not Vienna. This is not 1912. He turns around wildly to try to reopen the safety behind door **number six**, but it has locked behind him. The air buzzes like swarming hornets around his face, pricking at his brow, at his teeth, which chatter each understanding the flaw. In the apartment, he is safe, but out here, out here the world does not play the game by his rules. He clutches the papers to his chest and stares down into the darkening void of the chessboard floor. The walnut table with posy of post, and the door to the vestibule left open ajar, and the terrible buzzing like the traffic turned wild, and the papers burst from his arms like uncorked champagne to fill the staircase with fluttering moths. Reaching and grabbing to gather them up, they drift and they fall past the floor beneath him. Words, facts, disappearing from view. And the little red book punches the ground to spill cloth-board covers, and translucent paper and maps wrenched from the spine, and he can nearly reach. He can nearly reach.

The slap of doors and pulse of stair-bound feet descending from every room of Seventeen, Rushmore Terrace, replaces the quiet, pocket watch tick of Herr _____'s heart as it weeps ruby tears across the chessboard hall floor. It darkens papers and turns opaque the ghostly pages of the small, red Baedecker guide. Its punctured sheets, exhaled maps and detailed descriptions of Austria-Hungary as Karl Baedecker saw it in 1912, and from which the anonymous corpse had invented a life; still flutter airborne from the attic landing.

The assembled inhabitants, and absentee doctor who climbed the front steps and arrived through front door, to meet shattering skull upon monochrome tiles; listen to the proud growl of traffic beyond, and the porter admires the cut of the dead man's suit.

Jane Davis

The School Caretaker Polishes His Taps

'Kids!' he spits in his heart – once he was young.
He lights a fag and thinks, instead, of taps
worth a fortune in London if he'd go
but he goes nowhere. The school contains him.
Ducks into a lab to experiment
with words: 'Bitch. Bitch. Cow.' Predictable result:
acid churns the losses gut memory
– kids, house, car, time, heart, joy – she took the lot.

Girls at the locked evening door giggle,
call him 'Vic' for a laugh but he doesn't,
grunts 'None of your lip.' Their lips are lip-sticked
the lips of women, wife lips, liar lips.
'Passion!' her lips laughed. 'You don't know what it is.'
He lights a fag and thinks, instead, of taps.
Twenty-three pairs, antique, marble-topped,
Not repro, worth a fortune in London.

Behind his locked caretaker's door lovingly
he unwraps from greasy newsprint – bargains,
domestic murders, lonely hearts – his loves,
recognising autobiography:
shape without function, dried-up potential,
lays them out like mutilated bodies,
follows their curves with his cloth, feels the weight
of passion, sees his strange reflection there.

Magnetic Tape

Bush, thirty-five years old, this reel-to-reel
recovered from somewhere we had almost
forgotten and now Dad's thickened fingers
hesitate over the controls, bringing
your thirteen-year-old voice, deliberate
as the man you have become, up to pitch
in this then unimagined sitting room.

You sing to Dad and me across life's time;
before we met, before we knew, before
love married us. While I was somewhere else
you sang this barucha, this bar-mitzvah,
before you gave yourself to me, steady,
your young voice stunning the congregation,
and Dad, anxious, then sure, then kvelling.[1]

Over the keys and turning reels his eyes
half-absently meet mine. Time's banging around
the room, knocking the breath from our lungs, tears
struck out of us like joy, the man we love
between us, called up by molecules of tape,
'A Lifetime of Pleasure for the Whole Family'
miraculously still holding the boy.

[1] Yiddish for gushing, proud.

Alan Corkish

Liverpool, 1981

Do You Believe in Love ? [1]
        asked Huey in a glass case
        Kev's head nodded
          his agreement
singing with the Juke-Box music
enwrapping any woman
who came within
the compass
of his mile-wide smile
while in Parly above us
the sweetly scented petrol bombs piled high

---

[1] "Do You Believe In Love" was a song by Huey Lewis and the News, which was popular in the early 1980s.

Electric Memories

The right angled V of the sheltering tablecloth hanging almost to the floor separated the heavy, leather-laced shoes and moleskin trousers from the inches of brightly floral skirt, brown stockings and black, flat, shiny, patent shoes. The V was woollen and green and not nice to touch as silks and cottons were.

Baby sat, legs apart and with the big yellow truck between his legs. The truck that tipped the hard yellow, green and red wooden blocks so that baby could fill the truck and press the silver 'tip' lever again. Baby sat now watching the shoes and hearing the loud and unfamiliar noises. He sucked a big red block and felt with his free hand for the funny feeling that was in his tum, like when he'd eaten too much din-dins. Usually he liked being under the table but now the noises hurt his ears and his tum felt all funny.

Little Puss had run away to the far side of the dark beneath the table. Sometimes puss slept in the big yellow truck and baby pressed the silver lever and tipped her out but puss never minded. Puss was soft and nice to touch and baby liked to stroke her and to press his face into Puss's fur. Once Puss had licked the rusk crumbs from baby's chin with a warm, wet, rasping pink lick and baby had gurgled and threw his arms around Puss.

Baby loved Puss and Puss loved baby.

Baby didn't like the noise that was always growing louder and he didn't like the shoes that moved either. The shoes were usually still and Puss would rub up against them or lie still between them with the heat from the black grate (which baby had to keep away from) pouring on to her shell-striped furry back. Sometimes Puss would move her fat tail lazily to one side and then, ever-so-slowly, she'd move it back again as one or other of the shoes that faced each other stirred, but mostly she was still and the shoes were still upon the great rag mat. The great rag mat had lots of lovely colours like the yellow of the golden dust that fell from the flowers in amongst the seeding cabbages in Grandpa's allotment or the glowing red of Aunty Emma's lips. And it smelt dusty when baby was lifted from the tin bath to sit upon it whilst the white cotton towel with the big triangular patch sewn tightly in the middle made the skin near baby's neck tingle while the friendly brown hands rubbed him dry.

But now the shoes were moving. Moving towards the great rag mat and then back towards the pantry door but not moving like when they danced on special nights and baby was held high near where the gas-mantle hissed, not like that at all. The noise now was different and baby felt funny inside. Now the shoes moved like stabbing crab-nippers or the quick, scurrying rats that ran near the dustbins at the end of the lane.

The rats always made baby's tummy feel funny and full and hot and tight. Everyone chased the rats. Even Little Puss scrambled to follow them, as they ran away past the water tap that jutted from the red brick wall and which dripped water into the gutter. On and over the slated, moss-crusted roofs of the outside toilets they'd scurry and squeal with Little Puss showing her teeth and folding her ears back because she was not big enough to follow them. Baby didn't like rats 'cos everyone chased them and shouted very loudly, but Puss seemed to like rats.

Baby liked to watch the crabs with their green crab nippers when Da-da tipped them onto the floor from the brown cane basket that was shaped like a bucket and smelt like the sea. The crabs scuttled and stabbed but the big shoes hemmed them in. When they were dropped into the hot water they turned red but the nippers continued to wave in the steam and they were shiny and black at the ends... like patent shoes. Baby knew the nippers could hurt but he liked to watch the crabs.

The oil cloth was cool and wet-feeling on baby's legs. Under the table the green and white squares of the oil cloth were shiny except at each end of the table where large patches were scuffed gray-black and uneven. Outside the V of the woolen cloth and beyond the protection offered by the fat-round, shiny-brown, table legs, the bare parts between the rag mats were pitted deep with round, stabbed holes and long grey scrapes. Near the coal cupboard the green and white pattern had gone completely and all was a dull gray smear. A strong smell that lay over all the oil cloth was strongest beneath the table, it was a smell baby liked, it was the smell of washing day and soap and scrubbed white-wood table-tops.

In between the noises that baby didn't like, the crystal-set sang from the mantle shelf. 'Patience & Prudence' sang inside the brown box with the tight-stretched, brown-cloth front. The words that they sang were noises that baby didn't know but they too seemed different now and added to baby's tummy-tightness. Baby put his thumb past the big red block and into his mouth. It tasted of salt. Slowly, in the unfriendly darkness that now invaded his hiding place, he began to heave the tightness from his tum in heavy and uneven sobs. Puss looked up and shifted her weight backwards, snuggling small in her dark corner beneath the green woollen walls that encompassed them both.

*

Her voice seemed to reach his brain as if it were struggling through insuperable clouds. "Good God! Why have you stopped the car? Are you all right? God you're white as a sheet, I'd better drive...are you ill?"

At the side of the roadway, beneath the heavily fruiting branches of an oak, he sat behind the wheel of his car and leant his face against the coldness of the steering wheel re-living the scene from his childhood, remembering the baby-thoughts, feeling the baby-fear, picturing the event as though a videotape was being played inside his head. His stomach was tight as if gripped by those same baby-cramps. It was all so clear. So shiny-bright in his memory. The chessboard squares of the lino stabbed with patches of grey and black, fat brown table legs as hard as glass and reflecting his face as he pressed against the coldness, clean antiseptic smells and Puss wide alert in the far shadows, the rugs made of sacks threaded with rags of all colours and textures standing erect or splaying broken where feet had crushed them. The truck, the blocks, the cold-damp oil cloth and the two pairs of shoes scuttling to and fro. And the echoes from the car radio sparked the electric memories...Most clearly in his mind he could see the shoes because as a baby he had known that the shoes were connected with the noises that burned inside him and that they, in their turn, were connected with the sobs that shook his body...that shook it now that he was a man... and he knew that he was learning something new but that he couldn't understand what it was.

"Christ love, say something. You look like death..."; and she shook his arm. She was now leaning in the window on the driver's side. A light July breeze rippled through her hair. Passing cars beeped their horns. "Move over, let me drive."

"No. I'm all right now." He lifted his head and his face was pale. "It's that song, the song on the radio, that Patience & Prudence or whoever, it makes me feel sick inside. I hate that song... for some reason...come on, get back in. It's dangerous standing

42

there."

And when she resumed her seat she kissed his cheek.

"Shall we stay here a while ?"

But he shook his head lightly and pulled out into the traffic and the memory was already tucking away in his brain, tunnelling into the darkest recesses where it could sit and wait for another opportunity to surface when the time was right. One day, perhaps tomorrow or perhaps when he was old but before death released him, he would recall the final part of the scene, the part when baby realized what it was he had to learn. He turned the radio off. The scenes were fading. The song already forgotten.

*

The dazzling cacophony of smells, sounds, images and confusions rushed at baby, his whole frame shook and his tum was as tight as the skin on the blue and white drum. He crawled to the back wall which the table nestled against as his mother's body crashed to the floor with red smeared across her face. His tiny baby hand stretched out towards Puss in a fearful search for comfort when suddenly Puss struck out with her sharp claws and baby, with a movement as swift as the heavy shoes which bounced against his mother's body, grabbed Puss tight with one hand and struck her hard with the red, wooden building block. And then struck her again. And then again. Tiny red spots appeared over Puss's eyes and baby hit her even harder and 'Patience & Prudence' sang even louder and the tightness in his baby tummy made him howl and blood ran freely from the scratches in his hand and someone out there screamed a horrifying, nightmarish, mercy-seeking scream and the bitter taste of stomach-bile rose in his mouth as he squeezed Puss's limp body to his face and washed him with hot salt baby tears.

Lynn Owen

Lessons

the first time it happened
she was twelve years old
the whistle had gone
it was time to line up

she stood out
the grey school uniform
didn't camouflage her body

she was ordered to his office
he called her a naughty girl
she held out her hand
he caned her, she didn't cry

she tried hard to keep in line
but every Friday playtime
she stood out

she was ordered to his office
he called her a naughty girl
she held out her hand
he caned her, she didn't cry

Patrick Widdess

A Poet

"Kill it!" She screamed
at the sight of its vile body,
and hairy legs sprawled across the bedroom ceiling.
"It's just a harmless poet" I sighed,
reaching for an empty glass and the Sunday colour supplement.

Central heating

An icy draught blew up my trouser leg
as I sat at the dinner table,
so I tightened my belt and trapped it in.
The air warmed beneath the thick Corduroy
and my waist began to glow.

Soon the neighbours were coming round
to warm their hands around my belt,
and drape their damp socks and gloves over my lap to dry.
Small clouds of steam rose above my knees
and formed a cosy mist across the window pane.

Overcome

She paints a smile on her lips,
adorns herself with new clothes.
Each garment a cascade of colours,
clashing in joyful union.

Each day she takes two slices of bread;
soft, fresh, white.
No grains of fibre to grind the palette,
or make the stomach turn,
and tea, always China,
black, but not too black.

She reads once more his last words;
a hasty memo scrawled in chalk,
hanging, like a motto, on the kitchen wall.

Later she sits in her rocking chair,
as the sun rolls past the window,
embraced by its wooden arms.

Heading for the doorway;
she sees his face on the mantelpiece,
his coat still hung in the hallway,
and suddenly everything's changed.

Tom Sperlinger

View above Buttermere, 1999

A dual carriageway has replaced the street and where the houses on the other side were, there is a central reservation. Most of the houses on this side are semi-detached but this one stands alone. There are no flowerbeds in the front garden, just two squares of grass which are cropped short and end in rigid borders at the foot-path through the middle. There are no weeds on the path. As I stand at the familiar oak front door I look up and see the symmetrical sides of the house above me: they are painted white with vertical black wooden lines plunging from the eaves to the upper window on each side.

All of this is familiar. But I had forgotten about the pinch of shyness tightening my chest when I stood here, pushed forward to be first on the front step by my mother.

The pinch of shyness is there but it is my cousin Harriet who opens the front door. She still has the rapid blinking eyelashes of a twelve year old and she bites her lip in the silence after we mumble greetings. We hug awkwardly and I see that she notes the weight I have put on, though she says nothing. She asks about my journey and I tell her a few stories about unusual cars I have seen on the South Circular. I saw three of the new-letter number plates.

While I am talking, I watch her face. She looks barely awake and grey pods of skin are still collected around the edges of her eyes from the night. Her freckles stand out in relief against her pale skin which seems to stick in at pockets around her cheek-bones. She looks older or very tired.

There is a heap of unused coats on the stand. Aunt Mary's red raincoat is there and it looks as though Paul changed nothing in the house after she died. His walking sticks are also in the hall and the antique sideboard which was originally my grandfather's. The last thing which catches my attention is the mirror poking out from behind the coats, in which I can see Harriet looking at the raincoat and my own stomach protruding into view at right angles from me.

Harriet called me at the office. Paul and Mary did not have any children.

'I'm sorry to bother you at work,' she said. I thought she

was ringing about a favour she needed. I built a shed in her garden last summer. 'But it's Uncle Paul. Mrs Dunkerley rang me. He's dead.'

I do not like receiving bad news by 'phone. I noticed a few things. I saw for the first time that the clock on the wall to the right of my desk had a Mickey Mouse at the centre and not simply a splash of colour. I noticed that the fax I had just sent, still sitting on my desk, had the wrong date on it. I clicked the end of my biro twice.

'Who's Mrs Dunkerley?'
'His neighbour. She used to pop in after Mary died.'
'When did he ...'
'Last night, they think. A stroke.'
'He must have been ... well, at least ...'
'Eighty five. They think he died in his sleep.'
'I was always surprised ...'
'That he carried on so long after Mary died.'
'Yes.'
'I'm arranging the funeral.'
'Right'
'This Friday, at three o'clock.'

Harriet is making tea when her sister Sally and husband Jim arrive. Sally kisses Harriet, who leans back as their arms meet. It is clear that Sally and Jim have been fighting. Jim, a tall brusque bald man, is red in the face and stares distractedly into the space behind us all when he greets us. Sally's breath smells of gin.

We sit on the sofas at the back of the main room which is two rooms knocked into one. It stretches from the bay windows at the front of the house to the French windows and small garden at the back. This was where the adults sat when we were young.

Harriet sits in the corner by the windows. She is wearing a long black dress which leaves only her hands and face showing and her straight hair is tied flat to her scalp. She seems more in shadow because her head is bowed and her face turned half away from me. She bites her lip.

She has brought us all some tea and arranged a plate full of brown biscuits on the table. Sally sits on the sofa while Jim and I stand at right angles from one another with our hands in our pockets.

'You used to spend a lot of time here, Sal says?'

'Yes, I suppose we did. The motorway makes the journey much easier.'

Jim scowls. 'Not my favourite way to travel.' He walks forward a couple of paces and bends each leg in turn up behind his backside stretching out his driving muscles. He takes his glasses off and cleans them. Harriet pours the tea and we all sit down to drink it.

'Do we know who else is coming?' Jim asks.

Harriet mentions some neighbours and a few men who worked with Paul. There are three hours to pass before the service. Harriet mentions the will and says that she expects much of the furniture could be sold with the house.

'We can look over it again later,' Jim says. 'I doubt there'll be much competition for his Brentford season ticket!' He chuckles and looks round expectantly. Sally looks away.

I notice the watercolours which are still hung in lines around the room, paintings which Aunt Mary did of the Lake District where she grew up. I look from picture to picture. Some are quite clichéd. Small cottages with thatched roofs and rolling green hills. But others show a gentler touch. I particularly like a picture of a group of climbers resting to eat lunch. It is a picture I remember looking at as a child.

My eyes drop and meet Jim's which enlarge good-humouredly.

He asks if I heard the test score on my journey. I tell him the score as I last heard it, but it is nearly an hour since I arrived. We try to find news on the television, a wood-panelled set with a flow-ered tea-towel protecting the screen from dust. It has never been tuned in to Channel 4 and we both spend some minutes on our hands and knees fiddling with the black dials before we get a picture. Rain has interrupted play.

It has started to rain here too, though we have not noticed it until now. The apple tree behind the house is flapping its leaves gently on the windows in time to the floating wind, and drops land and slide on the screens. When we have finished our tea and eaten a few of the stale biscuits, I suggest we go for a walk if the rain stops.

Jim asks Harriet how her work is.

'I've been off sick actually,' says Harriet with a small laugh. 'I feel a bit of a fraud just lazing about with my feet up at home!' She looks round expectantly.

'How long have you been off?' I ask.

'Oh, about a month now,' she says. 'It's such a silly story. One of the boys in the sixth form was being disagreeable and I got into a flap. All very silly looking back on it. I just felt my eyes close, and woke up with my head, bang, like that' – she slaps her knee – 'against the desk. So I saw Dr. Coleman…'

A cousin from Canada calls soon after. While Sally talks to him and Harriet makes tea, I slip upstairs. I only want to use the bathroom but while I am peeing, I become curious.

Leaving the bathroom, I don't turn downstairs immediately but go into the back bedroom.

I remember the Lego mostly. I suppose none of us were extroverts as children; no show was made for the adults. When I first met my ex-wife she talked a lot about her family in Dublin, and the times as children when she and her sisters had sung and acted for their parents. But our play was confined to a quiet corner at the front of the house. There was often the sound of an ice cream van outside, but we did not ask to be taken out to it. I remember us sitting in a triangle building an igloo for our Lego men. Grandad or Uncle Paul had come over to see what we were doing and placed a hairy arm round Sally's shoulder. Grandad had bitter breath, a distinctive tobacco stench I have never come across since but none of us laughed about it.

I only remember us being together in this house. Certainly none of the relatives ever visited my parents. My mother and father would wake me at 4am to begin the long drive down from Birmingham. Uncle Joe came with Harriet and Sally. Their mother was dead. Grandad walked round the corner from his house behind the High Street.

Though the two rooms were knocked into one even then, the boundary was always re-imagined: the adults crowded onto the brown sofas and huddled round the small electric fire at the back of the house, all smoking. They were hidden from view because the back of one of the sofas was turned against the front section of the room. Not content with this division, we would huddle at the very front of the house leaving a few feet's distance from the grownups. Often we played where a crack of sunshine flowed through the window. It became a game one year to stay in the patch of light on the carpet. We did not leave this room for most of the day. We drew, the girls often read together and board games were produced.

We rarely played them. Quiet, industrious building with Lego was our favourite activity.

I remember spending a lot of my time there – probably while the girls were reading – counting cars. Not real cars, the Fords and Rovers on the streets outside, but the small, boxed toy cars which lined the walls of the front room. Paul collected them and most were still bound in their original air-tight boxes. There were classic cars and modern cars, police cars and fire engines. They were not so much displayed as set aside: too high for small children to reach with their mucky fingers, I suppose. I counted to ninety-eight one year and had only covered one side of the room. I was maybe four or five.

I have not seen the cars since arriving. But here they are, piled into sacks in a corner of the back bedroom. I had thought Paul would have sold them. They were not well off. Paul was redundant for the last ten years before he retired.

The majority are still in their boxes but they are piled without care. It is like a scrap heap of new cars. I pick up a red Mini and turn the box over in my hand reading the words on the back absently.

Other than the cars the room is the same. Very little light gets in because the window is small and overshadowed by the extension built on to the house next door. The wallpaper, small blue flowers, is still the same though faded. There are two dolls propped in a corner on the dresser which Mary must have knitted. On both dolls the cotton red cheeks are faded a milky pink.

I sit on the bed, which creaks as it always did. There are the same three books next to the lamp, Kingsley Amis's *Lucky Jim* and two science fiction titles I have never seen anywhere else. They are yellowing and dusty.

One of Mary's paintings hangs above the bed. It is bigger than the ones downstairs, the size of a tabloid newspaper, and contains a caption in Mary's curly handwriting 'View above Buttermere, 1929'. It is painted from high above the village of Buttermere, a few white buildings, with the lake further behind and smaller hills. There is a figure in red on a path ascending towards the painter.

The painting is familiar but I would not have remembered these details. It brings back a feeling. Of the crack in the ceiling, stretching from the bulb to the window which I do not raise my

head to look at now, of the smiling dolls in the corner and stale biscuits. This is what I think of as the view over Buttermere.

This is all that I wish to remember. I go downstairs.

It is the first funeral I have been to where nobody cries.

There are about twenty-five people in the church. Harriet
and I sit in one of the front pews. Sally and Jim are a few rows
behind. Harriet has a fragile but tuneful voice, and I listen to her
and sing only in whispers. We say a prayer, and one of Paul's
friends reads a Philip Larkin poem called 'Modesties' which I do
not recognise.

We stand for the second hymn.

> 'Let all thy converse be sincere,
> They conscience as the noonday clear:
> For God's all-seeing eye surveys
> They secret thoughts, thy works and ways'

Harriet was the first person I saw move, though she told me
later that it was Sally who left first. As I muttered the word 'works',
I watched Harriet collect her handbag and coat from beneath her. I
looked round and saw Jim go out of the door. Turning back to the
front, I saw the vicar. He was still singing, but looking towards me,
squashed his face into an exaggerated frown of sympathy. I felt
guilty that he had misunderstood.

Harriet and I looked at one another. She had stopped
singing. She bit her lip. We filed out of our pew, heads down, and
walked quietly out of the church. We could hear that the song had
finished and the vicar was starting to speak.

We stood on the green outside. None of us spoke. All of us
are smokers and Jim handed round cigarettes and we puffed
quietly.

Jim had found a stone and was kicking it from one foot to
another, making the exaggerated gestures of a footballer with his
arms. He kicked it towards the gate. It sped slightly above the
ground towards me. I swung my right leg back and gave the stone
an almighty whack. It flew faster than I expected, up towards the
church and crashed through one of the small windows to the left of
the door.

Jim looked at me, his mouth twitching into a smile. I looked
at Harriet. Harriet looked at Sally, and Sally looked at the floor. It

was Jim who started running. Half-way down Borough Avenue, I realised we were all running. All running and all laughing. By the time we made it the three blocks to the High Street, we had to stop. We were all panting for breath and trying to catch some air between laughs and puffs on our still lit cigarettes. We got some strange looks.

When we got home, Harriet and Sally cleared out much of the food in the kitchen while Jim and I watched the cricket on television. Later someone suggested a barbecue and Jim and I built a bonfire. Unlike the front garden, the back was untended and amidst the long grass there was a large pile of rotting wood which we decided to burn. When we had all had a bit to drink I slipped upstairs and asked Jim to come with me.

We got up to the back bedroom, and I pointed at the piles of cars.

'Are you …?' Jim began his question but looked at my face and did not finish it. We hauled the sacks downstairs and into the garden.

We threw them all on to the fire. Harriet threw the most.

Ben Newton

Apart From The Flame-Haired Horse Chestnuts

Apart from the flame-haired horse chestunts,
The sky remains green, although a parchment
Of hymnbooks lays transplanted at our feet.
We discuss the news, as we have done since we met,
Exploring our stale reaction, our autumn thoughts,
And our hands collide as if in happy accident.

Wendi Bestman-Sharp

Autumn Leaf

Autumn leaf –
Smoother than my mother's hand.
Her cold, damp cheek against starched pillow.
Clumsy movements through early morning darkness
My tiny magic
Tip-toe-tip-toe
Amidst clumpy shoes and electric underslips.

I run my chocolate button fingers across
The bulk of her leather purse.
The gold crocodile snap as I retrieve my prize.

Like a secret.
I disperse onto the warm landing
She did not stir.
I did not wake her.

Enchantment

She reminded me of a dinner lady I used to cling to
in my toddling, gravel grazed knee days: strong
mouth, deep set eyes – darkened like they worried too
much – slept too little, warm and wise.

One had to imagine her story – she was verbally recoiled.
I pictured her on brisk chilly morning walks, with an elegant dog;
Curled up in an old sofa, reading impossible books.
She was alone, but not always lonely – never easily warmed to
people, but cleverly disguised it and that special person could
learn to hold her gaze and crack a smile
on that well-formed mouth of hers.

I was like a full stop in comparison to her unwinding beauty and
mystery. Babbling and disclosing. Bawdy and crass, a menace
like a yapping puppy, a whining child.
Like a sleeping flower, her petals closed up
and what little hope I had of extracting a tiny scent from her, was
eroded by my malted behaviour.

It was cold and we were both wet – so I left upon her request,
struggling with a lump in my throat.
She had touched me.

Bill Dynes

Madness

Synopsis;
There is a trend that states that you are a non-person if
you do not wear the right clothes or weigh the right
weight. Compounded recently by the tucking in of shell
suit bottoms to designer socks.
Unfortunately, Argyle socks were mistaken for the real
designer thing. Which just goes to show.

Madness;
Madness – (*Not madness the group.*)
Just a small bunch of neurones, looping the loop
 inside my head.

I gaze at the world through rose-tinted eyes,
through lack of sleep, no great surprise.
'Cos the nightmares start when I leave my bed
and they're ten times worse when I rest my head.
Wandering corridors in my mind.
They're long and they're dark, and there's something behind
me.

I spy a doorway,
there, to my right.
With an exit sign glowing
green and then white.

There are chains and bars and bolts and locks.
And a woman stands beyond it dressed in bright green socks
 and – *nothing else.*

To the left of the door, there's a sign which reads…

THIS DOOR IS ALARMED.

So I s o o t h e it,
and it pleads with me:

The Liver Bards

"Let me out of this corridor…
I was the entrance to Woolworth before
you and your neurones brought me here."
The door beyond which almost nothing was dear,
but you'd often forget what you went in there for.

I reason that this is the fault of the door.

I move on.

A staircase now.
So slippery and steep.
At the top is a tower,
a castle, a keep.
Five million steps to the madness creator,
and half way up it's an escalator,

                        moving

                             down.

With a magic spell using dragons' droppings,
I conjure the trick used by Mary Poppins
and slide up the banister tall and proud.
Passing ghosts of my history, rending their shrouds
and throwing the shreds of them into my face.

"You're a Bastard, and Arsehole…A Fucking Disgrace"

I ignore them,
as I am wont to do.
Pass the same naked woman
this time in socks blue.

I move on.

I'm not sure exactly how far from the top
I am, when abruptly I come to a stop.
A landing leads off in two different directions.
Along one, a young man cuts his brain into sections.
The knife he is using is mother of Pearl–
       or Angie or Melanie or some such young girl
that he lost his heart to, and will never recover.

The Liver Bards

He's not learned that there is no such thing as a lover;
forever, endeavours to cut out the part
that attaches the eyeballs to strings of the heart.
So he won't see them tempt him.
He won't see them flutter
their eyelids, and skirt hems
and then make him mutter
                    and stutter.

And slowly dissection continues.
Until all that's left are the ears and some sinews.
The pain is all gone but the hacking continues.

                    I move on.

And there to his opposite side is another.
Who looks not unlike him a possible brother,
or maybe a clone, whom on closer inspection,
We find not alone and endowed with erection.
He writhes in some ecstasy hard to describe
to a mind closed tight-shut to a heart so alive.
And here in a corridor, dark and alone,
they'll sweat and he'll hump and he'll mumble and moan.

He thinks that the world outside won't understand,
and holds tight to another man's cock in his hand.
Until it is over, begun then again.
When all of the worship turns round to refrains
of his sorrow and guilt and of such hollow pain.

                    I move on.

And back to the stairwell resuming my seat,
a sprinkle of droppings, enchantment complete.
I gaze to the heavens, a spiral of steps
makes me dizzy and leavens the whole atmosphere.

All of a sudden up there at the ceiling
I see, like a light, at the tunnel's end reeling;
a myriad of stars in a circle of light
bringing hope and such comfort, such lurid delight.

The Liver Bards

Not the madness creator, I had at first feared,
That picked at my soul, as it had done for years.
Would I mourn for the control, this had over me?
Just a small naked girl, with white socks to the knee
The end of the banister, comes up quite soon
and I find myself landing, in one great round room.

Like the hub of a wheel, with more long corridors,
with a door halfway down each, and mirrors for floors.

What to do, do I choose?
The wrong one – do I lose?
There's no rulebook, nor history giving me clues.
I walk to the nearest and push at the door
and the stench of old memories I've known before
rushes out from the gap and I retch and then turn
and I run from the corridor, only to learn
                                        that...

I'm back where I started from;
foot of the stairs.
I'm back where I started
and nothing has changed
except now I see I ain't the one who's deranged.

It's just like a nightmare,
so real and surreal
which can trick all your senses
you believe that you feel.
You believe you're unworthy
cos' that's what's been said
from the time that you wake
'til your head hits the bed

                    Let's move on!

It's a great big lie people!

They'd have you believe that your socks are a measure of what
you'll achieve in this life.

Or your car, or your coat, or your name.
You are welcome, acceptable, winning, *the same.*
You have to conform to your peers' opinion
that you in your splendor, are simply a minion,
                                        like them.

This only proves, fears are not always true fears
just the fact you've been forced to believe it for years.
Just the madness of life
no, not Madness the group.
More a small bunch of neurones, looping the loop
in your brain.

Move on

Ruth Talmud

All to Zion

All broken clocks delay eventual fates,
Grind halt imminent judgements;
Knotted like muddled nets
Only posing questions regarding stopping time.

Unexpected vision will xodus your Zion.

The Hypnotist

Try as you might
you cannot resist
the magnetic eyes
of the hypnotist.

Battle and fight
you will not resist
the beautiful hand
of the hypnotist.

It is loose, it is tight
so hard to resist
the soul bleaching grip
of the hypnotist.

It is wrong, it is right
no need to resist
the heavenly path
of the hypnotist.

Robert Burman

Always a Pound

I often wonder why I chose to find love at a funeral. Other people also wonder. All I can tell them is that I don't know why either. It was my Uncle's funeral. Great, I think. Not great as in 'wow', but great as in distant. Not, that he wasn't great – he was. He had a gold smile; a gold tooth, the original lost in France. It was sad; the funeral that is.

I have a problem with funerals. Most people do. My problem is that I can't cry. Today I wanted to. I liked him and I wanted to cry.

Instead I chuckled; at a bee that landed on the coffin. It began sniffing at the flowers and I wondered if they smelt of funerals. I wondered what funerals did smell of. This one smelt of mouthwash and hairspray. Perhaps that's the smell of death.

She was on the other side of the crematorium. I spotted her whilst blurting out one of those modern hymns. The name escapes me – of the hymn; the name of the hymn – her name doesn't. It was Beverley. As in the town; although she didn't laugh when I reminded her of that. I couldn't tell why.

She was moving her mouth, in time, not singing. She said she hated singing in public. I said that she wasn't religious. I watched her mouth, and the organ played the wrong notes. I don't think it mattered.

During a prayer, I dropped my hymnbook. It was only her who looked round. I grimaced. She smiled, but I failed to notice as I scrabbled beneath some disapproving glares. As we all whispered 'Amen' for the last time, she dropped her hymnbook too, and I fell in love. Leaving the crematorium I saw the gold handles on the coffin and I thought of my Uncle's smile. I wondered if the handles could be used again.

She waited for me by the doors. She smiled. This time I noticed.

'Were you a relation?' She asked.

'Distant, yes. He was.' She was confused. I don't think I heard the question.

I held her umbrella as she buttoned up her coat. It wasn't cold, but she looked better that way. I felt as though it should have been drizzling, it may have added to the mood. There were some people sobbing, it made me feel better, at least I wasn't expected to cry.

'Beverley,' she said, and we shook hands. I later told her mine.

The tooth had been lost in a war, he had said. I was sad to learn that he'd chipped it on a stale baguette. We sat outside in the drizzle, and laughed at the joke. It was a joke that I had heard a lot, but it lightened the mood. There was smoke in the air, a cigarette butt rested on the step. Tears, from the smoke, trickled down my face whilst we laughed. My Aunt had just died, but my Uncle could chat.

I was on the step again. This time Beverley laughed, whilst I smoked. She hadn't heard the joke. I looked at the garden and thought how long it was since I had been to my Uncle's house. The apple tree had gone, and now the step was cold. We moved inside. The house was full, mostly with people I didn't know. They all seemed to be smiling. When I asked why, no one seemed to know. Beverley looked good in black. It was my turn to smile. I didn't know why.

I drank a bottle of wine and went back outside. Nobody appeared to be leaving. It was late and I was drunk. I was also angry, but that was the wine. Beverley found me in the greenhouse; I had fallen asleep with my head against a bag of peat. I was trying to re-pot a tomato plant. She laughed. I didn't hear. She took me home.

He smiled and gave me a pound coin. Always a pound. I grinned at him, whilst stuffing it in a pocket. He never asked what I was going to do with it.

When I woke up I made sure that I had a pound coin in my pocket. I also made sure that I still had Beverley's phone number. She was different now, brightly dressed and bobble-hatted. I laughed at the hat and refused to say why. We had a drink. She asked me about my Uncle.

'He was great,' was all I could say and we didn't mention it again.

This time I took her home, we kissed and I left in a cab,

thinking about my Uncle.

I went round to his house a few times whilst I was at university. The visits gradually tailed off until I just didn't go at all. I suppose that it was guilt that stopped me from going. People tend to think it makes you go, but it doesn't. Then, when I did go, he wasn't there.

I found myself sobbing in the back of the taxi. The driver glanced at me, puzzled.

'Pull over,' I said and threw him a few pound coins.

I crumpled on the kerb, then worked my way to my Uncle's. No one was there. I went round to the back and sat on the step, it was still cold. I bit my nails until Beverley rang.

I thumbed a pound coin in my pocket and thought about what they'd done with the gold tooth. Beverley arrived. I asked her what happened to people's gold teeth when they died. She laughed and said that she thought the gold tooth fairy got them. I shoved her playfully. She later complained it was too hard.

Beverley left and I sat for a while, thinking about nothing and then my Uncle. I went to the greenhouse, a tomato plant was flung across the floor. He would sit in here for hours. At night I thought that I could see his gold tooth, glinting inside. It was just a reflection. Dirty and tired I abandoned the tomato plants, leaving them sad and scattered.

Hannah Sheppard

Fragments of a Relationship

1.

If I uncross my legs and place my foot
A little further back
I can feel the gentle pressure
Of your knee against my thigh.
There is an innocent eroticness to this
Until my leg begins to ache
From being held in this unnatural position
Fearful of leaning fully onto you
I have to rearrange my legs again.

If I lean my chin
On my left hand and lay my right
Across the table
I can feel the gentle tension
As I wonder whether you
Will notice it is close enough to hold
In your left hand which is lying close by
But you don't take it
And it is time for me to clap again.

You made me laugh and
I tilted my head forward.
Bringing it back up
To look you in the eye
I found your lips waiting there for mine
To kiss and gently caress
No longer in an unnatural position
Leaning fully on you
And having to kiss you again.

Leaning my cheek
On the rough comfort of your
Coated shoulder
I smile as I watch my bus go by
Then nuzzle at your neck,
Wallowing in invisibility
As strangers pass us by
Comfortably knowing the pleasant fact
That it's half an hour before my bus will pass us by again.

3.

I told you about my coffee shop
'I want one'
'A coffee shop?'
'Yes.'
I told you about wandering in at midnight
And reaching for the brown covered,
Complete works of Shakespeare,
Embossed in gold,
From the shelves stacked with second hand books.
I told you about ordering an
Iced double mocha with whipped cream, chocolate sprinkles
And a long spoon with which to eat the cream,
While I read *King Lear*.
I told you about sitting in the slightly cooling
Hot sticky Denver, Colorado street,
Drinking my coffee, reading *King Lear*,
Watching the people around me
Drink their coffee, play chess, laugh,
Stare into each others' eyes.
I told you while you kissed my neck and
asked if you could come when I had one.

4.

I fell in love in Liverpool
In a café
In an attic
Listening to a poet
Who wasn't very good.

7.

Liverpool skies and I
Await your return
With warm rainbow tears
And tender kisses.

9.

A set of toes, at the end of the bed,
Bruised a shade of purple
By the varnish that catches the dimming light,
Flex and curl
Spreading themselves luxuriously.
My eyes fixate on them
Watching their every move
While you tear at me with your
Words
You pull apart my heart and start
On my soul
Until my eyes
Carefully cleanse
My cheeks.
I don't know what to say
I stare at the toes
At the end of your bed
Not fully conscious
That they are mine
And that a distant
Part
Of me
Survives.

10.

I say
I love you
But the words
Stumble clumsily
Down the phone line
Like a wrong note
Accidentally played in a tune.

Rachel Tunnard

To a flexible friend

You took me to heaven and back in a
few short months. Lost in our ecstasy,
we ignored the statements, and the people
who said I was foolish and frivolous.

And my father didn't approve; said I
should be studying not gallivanting
with you. But you made me so happy,
accepted everywhere, with cashback.

There wasn't a film I couldn't see, no
dress I couldn't buy, no CD sale....
And our weekends away, you'd even pay
for meals for my friends and me.

Little things, a bottle of wine, a pack
of fags, a £100 mobile phone
bill. You forever at my side, in your
silver, beautiful firm way. Such good times.

But they had to end. I think now you were bad
for me. We were too indulgent. I was using
you; I took advantage of you. Some said you
were always under my thumb but in the end

It was you who controlled me. Then it was
too late to switch. I'll always remember
you and the glowing feeling inside when
I was with you, down the high street with bags

Swinging. I cut you in two and had to
live without you. Maybe one day we'll be
reunited. If I keep within my
overdraft limit.

Andrew Taylor

Cathedral I

September, a new season, start to the year.
Students settling in rented accommodation.

Cathedral Close three storeys, baring the brunt of
the river's breath. Weakened sun, tower sends shadows.

*'Visitors were beginning to approach the Cathedral through
a tangle of urban decay'*

Gambier Terrace blocked by leaves, not yet yellowing
Triangle of streets, spotted with cars.

Scott's vision, integration. Isolation on the Mount.
Washington Street, inspirational gateway, past.

*'Many people do regret the passing of the grassy slope
down to Great George Street'*

Cranes angled against dark Autumnal skies. Familiar
to office workers city-wide. Horizons change monthly.

Sighted from lines that run to Lime Street, from across
the water. Embedded in minds as firm as the rock below.

Addendum I

Vaulted ceilings viewed inside out.
Cast concrete supports like a disused
Underground station white, waiting for
the ghost train de-icing unit.

*I never get sick of looking across the
city to it.*

Corona Gallery walkway just wide
enough. Hard hatted workmen harnessed
up, preparing to battle with December's
wind. Scaffold ice cold.

*The ravens are back. The work'll have to move
to the other side.*

Frost dusts sleepers where the sun hasn't
hit. Mist hangs on the river. Up the hill
skyline shrouded mystery for late season
tourists.

The best views are from the ferry.

Candles burn in Mathew St. petals scatter
like confetti. 21 years on remember
bringing home the news, ready for Ready
Brek.

Somebody spent two hours hand drilling the door.

Macdonald's model for the West Porch.
Particles swirl, patterns intricate as
drawings from Lincoln's Inn Fields. Chest
open, dark ink on grey paper.

The flags come here to die.

Lines Written in Early Autumn

September sounds, clear sky. Parliament
Street shadowed by Customs and Excise.
Scaffold rises over Kings Dock, glints in morning sun.

'The last thing I said to you is don't leave me here'

Piano plays alone. Tracey's beach hut
weather beaten. Screech of seabirds competes.
Encased behind double windows, safe from the
incoming tide.

*'Talkative. This particular image is of Adny (left)
and Billy (right)'*

The ACL leaves Seaforth. Horizon clear.
Wind Farm scything. Three Graces elegant,
familiar. Picture ships queing to dock. Pier Head
as bus terminus.

'On a clear day glimpse the lighthouse at New Brighton'

Wrapped. Regeneration agenda driven. Try to
move THAT on hydraulics. Windswept. Lasers
guided through melodies. Torn apart. Expectations
turn sour.

'Love is the contdition of being human'

Skateboarders gather in Chavasse Park. Yellow
Submarine graffiti cleared. Bins upturned, pathways
scattered. New shoes rub, feet ache. March towards
'The Egg'.

'See it as conducive to quiet contemplation'

Lighthouse. View from a rush-hour train. Canal
still, reflecting locks. Jetsam gathered. Shingle
towpaths unworn, BAT building halved. September
sounds, evening skies dusk settles like stardust.

Waveform

(for Stanley Sidney Smith English)

> *Waveform (phys): a graph showing variation of amplitude
> electrical signal, or other wave, against time*

Sleek in black cast aside
as forgotten dream
pigeons clap on take off
circle above seeking
scattered crumbs

Waveform quiet unobtusive
curling like budding ferns
wind unable to reach scuttle
through create a sound poem
of crashing waves

Erosion carried on sea air
biting in while Edward VII
greens on horseback with his
better river view public access
of no concern

Mysteries unsolved foundry
secrets kept lost archive records
taking public air space humbly

Helen Harper

From Millions of Nuts and Bolts

At the start of the marathon I was suddenly enveloped by bodies. The heat that they generated plus the pervading smell of liniment and after-shave took my breath away. I put a trusty polo fruit in my mouth but it made little difference. The cracks and jokes stopped and there was a sort of loaded silence as people checked their stop watches, race numbers or kit. Peoples' faces: you can tell so much from looking at a face, even a silent face. I took a sweeping glance at a few. Big mistake. Most people looked drawn or apprehensive. No matter. I looked at the floor instead, pulled the cap down over my eyes, and made a mental body check: Head, not sure; heart, beating fast; chest, breathing too fast; stomach, settling down; bladder, empty but feels full; arms, loose; legs, tense; feet, a bit large but okay. It doesn't matter how nervous I get in the build-up to a race, whenever I line up with everyone else I get excited. As I looked over at the starter's raised gun, I felt my tension beginning to unfold imperceptibly and almost reluctantly, but it was getting there. At the sound of the first bullet I moved; slow and easy, yet even before the sound of the second bullet I was moving rapidly and in good rhythm, flying low, on top of my running; fit, healthy and strong. Four thousand pairs of legs left Camp hill, Springwood avenue... and all that remained was a smoking gun.

The route of the marathon was to take us past Sefton Park, along the Dock Road, onto the Pier Head, along Otterspool promenade, through Aigburth, Garston then eventually back into Woolton. Crowds of spectators had lined the roads and either waved or cheered, clapped or shouted us away onto our journey. I'd made sure that I had placed myself right in the centre of a large group, running along with them for the first 6 miles or so, because I got embarrassed whenever people clap if I'm running along on my own in any road race. Most of the runners were blasé about the next few hours of running that lay ahead of them, but I could sense that they were more than a little concerned about the distance involved. I knew I was: because I had trained hard for this marathon, I knew that the first 13 miles were well within my capability, anything after that distance and I was in no-man's land and in deep trouble. Forget all that about hard work; being fit and deter-

mined, being focused on the race to get through the last 13 miles…
I knew that I was set to hit the wall, big-time, at some stage past
the halfway mark.

The route was well marshalled with helpful mile-markers,
at least they were for the first 6 miles, after this, my heart sank into
my running shoes at the sight of them as they nonchalantly
informed me that I'd run 8 miles but I could have sworn it was
much more than that. Someone to my right ran into a traffic cone
and went sprawling onto the road, people stopped to help him and
although I was sorry for his plight, I was glad it wasn't me.
Because of the heat, extra water stations had been set up every 3
miles and although we had been advised to take on water at every
station, I had decided to leave my first drink until after the first 5
miles rather than have the sensation of it sloshing around inside me
as I ran along.

During miles 11 and 12, I took to reading peoples' backs.
Some wore the official shirt of the sponsors, but others had spe-
cially printed, or designed jobs which interestingly (or
uninterestingly, depending on what mood you were in) informed
the world behind them that; 'I'm only Rock 'n' Roll but I'm doing
my best' or, 'stop me if I'm getting ahead of myself'. An approach-
ing water station broke the monotony and I watched the different
actions of some runners who, rather ungraciously, snatched the
plastic cups of water out of the hands of offering marshals without
even a thank you; others stopped to drink but their legs didn't look
too steady; some ran skilfully drinking at the same time without
spilling a drop or looking like an out of control idiot, mostly people
settled for just pouring the water over themselves.

As we ran through Bootle I noticed a large sign just ahead
of me, it read 'MILLIONS OF NUTS AND BOLTS', it was adver-
tising a trade warehouse I think. Looking along the endless chain
of runners that stretched out into the concrete distance, listening to
the various moans, and groans, grunts and creaks that surround me
on all sides, this sign seemed so apt. It would take a million nuts
and bolts distributed among so many runners to replace, or hold
together the different body parts that had either worn down,
dropped off, turned in, or gone home. I got into a conversation with
a person who, even without my glasses, I could see was not at all
bad-looking. We swapped horror stories about the rapid deteriora-
tion of our bodies over the previous 2 hours or so and we were
getting along fine until he told me that he was 17 (my God!) I nerv-

ously looked around for his mother, or even worse, his big sister before rapidly moving on.

Running along the Dock Road lifted my spirits. People who had come out of pubs to watch us offered their pints of lager, bitter or mild to the passing runner; some stopped and took a small amount. Further along, Radio City had set up a bandstand and had put together a compilation of songs that contained the words 'run' or 'running'. *keep on Running* (highly original); *Running Scared* (highly appropriate); *Run For Home* (highly tempting). Someone had connected a hose-pipe from one of the pubs which enable us to run through a makeshift but very welcome shower. From behind me another runner shouted good-naturedly 'you could've at least connected it to the beer pump!' The owner of the hose-pipe shouted back immediately 'this is connected to the beer pump, mate!'

At 19 miles my face had started to melt, it felt like it was burning, alternating between a deep shade of red and a worrying shade of grey; my eyes were dark because they were sinking fast. And THE HAIR! Nightmare or what?! I had so carefully tucked it up into my cap at the start, it was, by this point, sticking out at all angles, the parts of the hair that didn't touch my face or neck bobbed along in all directions completely out of rhythm with my running. I pushed my cap up and away from my face and eyes, mainly to allow my forehead to breathe and cool. I knew I looked odd but I was past caring.

'Keep going' lad, not far now'. Two points I told him mentally; point one; 7 miles to go is far when you're running a marathon; point two, ahem, I'M A W-O-M-A-N!!

I'd never run this far, ever. I was really tired and hungry but everyone else was experiencing the same thing (at least I hoped everyone else was suffering like me.) I concentrated on following two men who were steadily plodding along but I had the growing awareness of someone quite close behind me. Although I'm quite an easy going person I felt a surge of irritation because if he clipped me, being tired, I knew that I would fall over. But I wouldn't just fall over, I'd go down like a ton of bricks and probably take out the two guys in front who I'd been tracking and what would be another matter entirely. I could hear his breathing within close proximity of my neck. I normally enjoy a man breathing heavily against my neck, especially if a) there was a reasonable amount of deep shadow or the lights were out; b) he passes for something vaguely resembling a human being; c) I fancy him; d) he's sexy; e) he knows what he is doing and doesn't start slobbering; this was not one of those men, and definitely not one of those occasions. His breathing was annoying me as he was so close. I decided to turn round and politely tell him to go away:

'Hey, will you fu...oh hi John!' It turned out to be a man I knew slightly from work; he started talking to me and I despaired; he's a nice person but I was not in the mood for small talk at that moment in time. He informed me that he had 'runner's nipple' – wonderful. This is a condition that happens mostly in male runners, the friction and sweat from the tee shirt causes irritation, it's mostly uncomfortable but at worst it can cause a small amount of bleeding, Vaseline helps. He asked me if I was holding together okay and I mumbled something about my sore left knee but after such physical exertion I seemes to have lost not just the power of hearing but also the capacity to understand and respond to simple conversation. My eloquent replies to the usual enquiries about how I was feeling, how fast had I gone, my preparation etc all consisted of either a grunt or 'Uh?' 'Eh?' 'N' or 'Y' He left me pretty soon and I couldn't imagine why.

As I glanced up, the line of runners still snaked into the distance and I felt encouraged by the fact that no-one around me had stopped to walk, despite the moans and groans and complaints about the heat or wanting to go home. Still we ran on, we followed as if under the irresistible magnetism of an unseen Pied Piper. Suddenly the thought struck me that the Dock Road was never going to end and for a bizarre moment I nearly started crying. I told myself I was going through a bad period, I hadn't just hit the wall with a thud that would frighten the cat, I'd crashed into it like a demented squash ball with all the certainty that there was definitely no bouncing back from this.

I wanted to stop, badly. I started wishing; wishing I'd had a bigger breakfast; wishing I could recapture my feelings about this marathon at the beginning of the race; wishing I'd not started off so quickly for the first 5 miles; wishing I could glide along gracefully and majestically like those runners you see in a little pack at the front of any road race called 'elite'. Oh but most of all, most of all, I wished that I was blonde. I could do blonde, no problem, I could run along with a mane of pure blonde hair trailing behind me in the wind, no, better still; bouncing around my shoulders, running along and looking great. I wished I was blonde with big blue eyes because I'd read somewhere that blondes have more fun. Instead I'm not blonde and looked like a cross between Ken Dodd and Jerry Lewis caught in a particularly madcap mood with my hair running wild and a stupid goofy expression fixed firmly on my face.

I wasn't sure which was worse, the glaring sun in the sky or the heat that rose up from the floor, hitting me full in the face, before, slowly proceeding to travel the entire length of my body, down to my toes and then back again in the same maddening cycle. Droplets of sweat fell from my hair to settle or rove in different locations of my head or body; they rolled slowly down my forehead and into my eyes before settling onto my eyelashes, and, rather than wipe them away, I just lowered my eyes and waited for the tentatively hanging beads to either melt or fade to the floor; the droplets also fell to lick and probe along the shape of my ear before seeping inside and playing there. Its physical agitation was like some bizarre audio orgasm making me lose concentration for a while but I stayed with the feeling because I liked it. Droplets rolled from my neck, along my back, seeping into my running shirt. God! I was so hot, I was sweating like a man and it was making me sexy. Wow! That's something the running magazines don't tell you about! I was drained, hot, wet, aroused and … pissed off.

The notion suddenly occurred to me that I could collapse and die right there. I know people do die running marathons but at that moment the thought of such a fate happening to me seemed like a luxury; the ideal excuse to just lie down. Lie down… Would I ever regain the ability to do such a thing after being upright and stiff for so long? Still, I did have this irrational urge to finish the marathon while I was still young enough to go through the motions of what passes for breathing.

I didn't realise it at the time, but I was dehydrating because I hadn't taken on any water except for a small amount before the start. I felt shaky and sleepy, my lips were dry and starting to chap. I regretted not having brought along some Vaseline to use on them. I really needed some water and as I approached a water station I sensibly decided to renew my acquaintance with the stuff and immerse myself in it. As I stopped, I took deep calming breaths but my hand was shaking as I raised the plastic cup from a seemingly endless table that had engulfed the entire length of pavement. It looked like I was in the middle of a summer street party. Two more tables to my left piled, not with food but adorned with numerous plastic cups and large hand-written signs informed me that table 'A' contained water; table 'B' contained orange juice. Balloons and multicoloured decorations hung overhead completely still in the afternoon air; they looked how I felt; miserable, limp and suffering in the heat.

I held my cup in one hand then gingerly ran two fingers over my lips, almost teasingly and in preparation before reaching down and inserting them into the cool moisture; removing them, my moistened fingers gently rubbed along the lips, a soothing trail of lubrication that traced their outline and shape. Under this slight pressure the lips parted involuntarily yet gratefully to allowed the roaming tips of these fingers to deposit a thin healing line of cool water just on the inside in slow circular motions, a wet, tactile exploration. It hurt. I drew as much liquid as I could past my lips, sucking but trying not to gulp, allowing it to roll over and around my tongue in a sensuous tease, chasing, enjoying and savouring the feel of its fullness in my mouth for as long as I could before letting it slip away with a feeling of reluctance. I repeated the process with a second cup of water, again trying not to slurp and gulp too much but no-one seemed concerned with table etiquette; we all sounded the same anyway. My third cup of water was poured over my head, further cups, around my sports socks soaking my trainers and feet trying to flush out the heat. I watched as one woman put a sponge half way into the back of her shorts and carried on running, I thought she looked daft. Grabbing two soaking sponges, I washed my face with one and shoved the other half way into the back of my shorts and took off again.

As we entered the promenade the change of scenery seemed to lift everyone's spirits. Before entering it you could hear the moans and groans, weeping and wailing, gnashing of teeth, starting up again (and that was just the race marshals!) This was the nicest part of the route and the hot summer's day had brought quite a few hundred people out to watch or cheer; they lined the length of the grass verge and railings, shouting, clapping or cheering members of their family, friends or just about anyone who followed behind them, so no-one felt left out or neglected. I thought that there might have been a refreshing breeze along this stretch but no, it was still very humid. I looked toward the river and wished I was in it. Although I was trying to concentrate, my mind wandered as I glanced in the general direction of New Brighton and I imagined that I was sitting on top of a giant sandcastle eating a dozen lolly-ices and ice-creams at the same time without a pause.

As we ran through Aigburth people were standing outside their houses offering the runners food and drink. Two women had made plates of sandwiches and biscuits; they very soon had a small group of hungry people surrounding them. I was like a greedy little butterfly with the appetite of an elephant flitting from plate to plate, sampling the diverse offerings. By the time that I had remembered I was aiming to finish this marathon in under 6 hours, I had masticated (and half-choked on) pineapple chunks, peanuts, cheese sandwiches and a handful of chocolate fingers; it was the best Sunday lunch that I had ever tasted. The humour and light-hearted atmosphere of the Dock Road plus the generosity and kindness of the people of Aigburth and Garston remain vivid, outstanding memories of an event famed and feared for its discipline and endurance but one that is only made magical and special because of its spontaneity; it's not until it is gone that you come to realise this.

Eventually the familiar mile marker loomed in front of us again, impassively informing us that we had reached 25 miles but I didn't want to believe it. Although it was the last mile and I was in a part of Woolton that I knew well, I was beginning to wish I was blonde again; if I was platinum or a peroxide blonde I just knew that I could have run the marathon in 4 hours instead of 5 hours 45 minutes. Blondes really do have more fun. Actually I didn't really believe this, but I had to blame someone for the heart-breaking sensations that were coursing unchecked through my body. There was one measly mile to go and I didn't think that I could finish. I needed to find some energy and some distracting ideas but my energy had deserted me some 3 hours back and the only good distracting idea that I could think up … was to STOP! I thought about fucking and other bad habits. This proved a bad idea as my 10 second lustful fantasy only worked to tire me even more, such was its energetic content; besides, I'm not that kind of girl. I thought about Presley in '56, at his peak, aged 21, greasy hair falling over black, heavy-lidded eyes, sideburns protruding into his pale skin and acne…yet still a disarmingly beautiful boy from the South. He caressed and stroked the microphone in a deceptively gentle way as if it was almost part of his body and yes, you could almost trust him but for the sneer on his lips and the rhythmic hip thrusts; a hoodlum whose sexuality has run rampant and is now a menace to every father's daughter held captive in his audience. Lewd, suggestive and deliciously 'obscene', driving the establishment to distraction by refusing to tone down his stage performance of *Hound Dog* on the *Milton Berle Show*, which caused outrage. Such accusations were not without foundation but it was also obvious to me that he was genuinely cool, dangerously sexy...and real gone. I thought about myself in '73, aged 13 and listening to his records in the darkness of my bedroom with a guilty feeling that I should really be listening to the Osmonds; it is not until many years later that I came to realise what a source of comfort and companionship his records and films brought to a life and time that was often lonely, frustrating and troubled. I thought about Presley in '77, dead at 42, fat, reclusive, ugly, drug-ridden and amongst all the false tributes, crocodile tears and 'sensational' books that have merged into one throughout the years since his death, there is now for me only one thought of Presley, only one personal tribute to him that I can possibly think of...and that is a wish with all my heart that he had remained in Tupelo and become a truck driver, foregoing any pleasure of what it would mean to have had an Elvis Presley in my life. I thought. I thought about food, books, writing. I thought about finishing first and I thought about finishing 3,999th.

Yet none of these thoughts could take away the pounding in my head, it felt like it was going to burst; I could see the headlines; 'EXTRA! EXTRA! WOMAN'S HEAD EXPLODES ON LAST MILE OF MARATHON!" I removed my cap, my hair flopped forlornly over my face, damp irregular-shaped curls that stung my eyes, covering them, yet offering no relief from the sun's glare.

I noticed large numbers of runners, having already finished, making their way somewhat gingerly towards cars that resembled small ovens in the heat. They were appropriately wrapped in silver foil capes all prepared for those ovens! Those silver capes are commonly distributed at the end of any road race over 10km distance, I've always declined to use one because I always think they look ridiculous even though the idea behind them is to keep in warmth. As I re-entered Camp Hill all I could see around and ahead of me, standing, lounging or lying down, were bodies encased in silver foil.

As I ran along the finishing straight I hate to think what I looked like and I hope I never find out. I caught sight of my family as I crossed the finishing line but was immediately lost to them again as I was swallowed up by the hundreds of other finishers who were themselves aimlessly wandering around looking for their families and other supporters. A large medal was placed around my neck and I was happily looking ridiculous; at last encased in my silver foil cape, an advert if ever there was for sartorial splendour!

I was growing aware of the soft cushion of grass beneath my feet as opposed to hard, punishing concrete. My body was beginning to familiarise itself with the sensations of the regular motion of running having come to an end and I felt the build up of a severe discomfort, some black and monstrous promise of revenge from my body for having subjected it to such rigours over the past 5 hours; it came in the shape of aching in my back and shoulders with the gleeful promise of more to come and I felt a profound sorrow for my muscles, legs, feet and lips. It was a strange feeling. My body had stopped but I was still out on the road somewhere, still carrying the sounds, smells, sights and sensations of an extraordinary day and journey and it was difficult to come back to reality. I rolled over onto my back, hot 'n' bothered; normality was determined in its persistence to find a path that would allow it to slip back inside my body, persuading, nudging, and prizing against my half-protestations. I groaned inwardly not really wanting it. But, it finally pushed through, at times sliding away but immediately coming back with overpowering force and bearing down hard infusing my whole body with an invitation to respond. It hit the spot at last and suddenly I couldn't resist. It came in the shape of my family talking excitedly about the day; it came from sounds that blared from loudspeakers; music, instructions or greetings all of which intermingled in the most annoying fashion. It came from the growing awareness that the magic atmosphere of the marathon was fast disappearing; it came from sounds of exhausted runners who still managed to find surplus energy from God knows where to relate what a disappointing/ fantastic/ strange experience it was to run the course and cross the line to finally collect their medal.

But worst of all it came with the smell of grass and body odour mixing uneasily inside my nostrils making my stomach churn. I was really going to be sick. I decided to find a place for myself, crawl off quietly and curl up, but someone grabbed my hand in a sweaty grip shaking it firmly; it was my friend from the Dock Road. As I'd always been told that it was rude to vomit over someone while they are shaking your hand, I stifled the impulse, swallowed hard and thought of England. He asked me about my knees, I asked him about his nipples. One of my children ran up to me and shoved a half-melted Mars Bar into my hand; it was Lynda and she has beautiful blonde hair and deep blue eyes; it was her that I'd been focusing myself on for most of the day during my 'blonde moments'. FOOD! After having congratulated myself on keeping the contents of my stomach in its natural environment I felt confident enough to actually eat again. It took me 1 second to rip the paper off, 12 seconds to guzzle the chocolate bar and a further 12 seconds to puke it all back up again (amongst other items courtesy of Aigburth and Gaston!) I sheepishly looked around to see if a) anyone else had/was being sick and b) to see if the Brookside cameras were still rolling and recording my plight, destined to appear in some future episode as an unexpected and unpaid extra doing unsavoury things in the background, caught in glorious technicolour and everyone who knew me, leaning forward in their chair and saying 'isn't that Helen?'

Katherine Bainbridge

Emi

She sleeps
the ill-paced wheezing
Old age has brought her
Tartan blanket
Pulled to her chin

I asked her why
She married him
round faced shopkeeper
Twenty years her senior

Sometimes
She laughs
When she tells me
Of her childhood
Her face a mass of time worn folds.
My questions lost
In present time

Fifty years a widow
Great distance in her milky eyes
Why I married him?
She says and smiles
Security
For when the parents die.

The Holy Cow

My father owns a cow
With purple painted horns
Fat, for every day
My mother fetches
Reeds and grass upon her head

All day it chews
Knowing its importance
And makes us milk
Today my mother
Walked for miles
Came dripping back
Through monsoon rain

We like our cow
But I like best water buffalo
They wallow
And look funny when they run

Lucky Sons

In a hole dug by the road
Three women
Shovel stone

Straight backed
Metal pots piled high
Upon their heads
They load it to the van

Midday desert sun
Burns hard
Upon their hands
Bright sahris trailing
In the dust

In the cab
A shady place
Their brother sleeps
Fine healthy man
And waits 'til work is done

Constant
Uncomplaining
Smiling. Sometimes singing
They accept
This life

For Indian women
Have always worked
Yet still they pray
For sons

Naman Yasin

A Journey Back to My Roots

Here I was finally, at Islamabad international airport. Pakistan, my 'homeland,' my 'roots,' my 'true' identity, or so I was told, but soon brutally and harshly I learnt for myself, what I had entered was a totally different world. A world I did not know existed. Taking my first step outside the aeroplane was like walking into a gigantic oven, with the door slammed shut behind me. Immediately I felt nervously fearful of the unexpected, alienated and alone in a foreign land, despite it being my second home. The heat was so intense I could hardly breathe, barely wanting to breathe. Now there was no turning back.

One by one I was struck by the heat, culture shock and total disorganisation. Sometimes I felt a part of it, sometimes a complete stranger. Yet little did I know what fate had laid out ahead for me.

Checking out of the airport would, in England, take a mere twenty minutes. However, in Pakistan it was like an everlasting panic, which was not only emotionally but also physically draining, especially after a ten-hour flight. "Is this you?", a greedy immigration officer asked me sharply, referring to the photograph in my passport.
"...Yes..." I replied after a moments pause, baffled by the basis of his bizarre questioning.
"This is not you," he insisted, glaring at me.
I felt stunned and was left in despair; somehow I gathered the energy to carry on.
"Of course it's me," I protested, but to no avail. He was refusing to allow me entry to a country which together with Great Britain I held dual nationality, something he knew full well. Yet this greedy man was purposely tormenting me in hope of receiving a bribe, on the pretext that the photograph in my passport was not me! Any sane person would have clearly recognised it was my passport with my photograph in it. Finally, remembering my mother's words of advice before I left England, I paid him a bribe of twenty rupees (approximately twenty five pence), before reluctantly tackling my next hurdle of attempting to retrieve my baggage.

In true Pakistani style, the four hundred or so strong army of passengers from my flight flocked around the single baggage line to retrieve their luggage. Adopting the policy of 'every man for himself,' people were pushing, shoving, shouting and screaming whilst attempting to identify, before grabbing and dragging any suitcase or bag that vaguely looked like theirs off the speedily moving baggage line. Even if this meant that they themselves were being dragged along the line, with what they thought might be their baggage, through crowds of people competing for a front line position along the side of the line. The thought of other people walking away with their luggage seemed to inspire and stimulate these people, myself included, to act in a manner that neither helped themselves nor others.

Soon I recognised one of my two suitcases. Somehow I managed to squeeze through the crowd around me and drag my navy blue, huge and heavy suitcase off the line. Next I faced the daunting task of guarding the suitcase I had managed to obtain whilst simultaneously watching out for my other pink one, in case anyone decided to walk off with either. Trying as patiently as I could, I attempted to keep one eye on the line and the other on my suitcase beside me as I waited. People began to slowly trickle away from the line, having gathered all their baggage on broken trolleys, that evidently had been overused. Rather than moving in straight lines they were uncontrollably jerking side to side in a zigzag fashion, in a net forwards movement knocking anything or anybody out of their way. Meanwhile, I waited and waited. Once everyone had dispersed I was left hopelessly watching the same unclaimed suitcases go round and round again and again, with no sign of my pink suitcase. I had almost lost all hope and began descending from a tired to a depressing mood, when finally it emerged. I was so overjoyed it took a few moments to believe that it was actually my bag. All this had blanked my mind and I was barely conscious of where I was or what I was doing there. But soon everything came back to me. There are moments in life so stunning, so amazing that they are difficult to absorb. I had managed to pile my suitcases onto my trolley before walking out, when such a moment occurred.

My loving grandparents, uncles, aunts and cousins, many of whom I had never met before, recognised me first. I quickly glanced at the two photographs of them my mother had given me.

It was really them, standing impatiently behind a fence and yelling for me. As soon as physically possible they all gathered around me, hugging and kissing me. I felt so humbled; these people were my family who really loved me, yet I hardly knew them and vice versa. They immediately took over my luggage and like a superstar they hurried me past the harassing porters, beggars, vendors and vagabonds before bundling me into an awaiting van and driving me away to our family village. My journey had only just begun.

Pete Miles

Boring

They say I'm boring
I guess they're right
Cos when it comes to late at night
And people jive and jump around,
I go and make holes in the ground
With my drill and spike and corer
I can be a major borer.

Meena Chauhan

Screaming Silence

Crystal vapours fill your eyes
as you stare through the window
thinking of the birth you gave
the way you worked a life away
legs curled upon the cream settee
sinking backwards your head – haloed
by a mass of wiry curls –
cushioned somehow you seem lost
there's a distant anger surrounding
you. Words, questions bounce off
you unheard, unheeded.
What's the point, you whisper
as another tear falls. The missing
part of you inside is visible to me
I cringe at the acrimony we exchange
The unforgivable way we behave…

Nothing Lasts

XXXNothing lasts…
Forever cries memories fade
Falls to shards with time
[more like disappears with pain]
somehow I'm grasping
[futile]
at the pieces. With contact
I'm scratched: vampyre blood.
Untouched. The pieces drop
[elituf]
let go somehow
[pain disappears more like replaced]
time I want to readhere
memories blank Forever dies
…Nothing lastsXXX

March Attitude & Angry Sighs That Echo Along Into April

The world with its blues and greens and clouds
that cluster like families disgusts me.
Its people: men and women, that traipse vicariously
over a set play stage
dressed in fabric woven from ethereal
falsities. Appearances collide head first
with Truth and
Reality is a framed work of post-modern
art hung above an electric fireplace.
Flash cars – red speed –
looks of emerald envy, the leather interior
breathed in: inhaled like cigarette smoke
puffed out from mouths that kiss numerous
bodies.
Dreams are a lampshade that hold the
true blaze away, temporarily distracting
cunning shadows that scatter and hide
at the sight of minds that intellectualise.
Injustice gnarls the innocence of hearts
that now, as granite, can disguise former
pretence. Families like clustering and
cloud the greens and blues that would
otherwise unleash my internalities.

Anthony Evans

Ambition

One day